CLOCKS AND WATCHES
in the collection of the Worshipful Company of Clockmakers

Plate I
Table clock by Henry Archer, England c1625 *(catalogue number 584)*

CLOCKS AND WATCHES

*The collection of
the Worshipful Company
of Clockmakers*

*Cecil Clutton
and George Daniels*

SOTHEBY PARKE BERNET
PUBLICATIONS

© The Worshipful Company of
Clockmakers 1975

First published 1975 by
Sotheby Parke Bernet Publications,
Russell Chambers, Covent Garden,
London WC2E 8AA

Edition for the United States of America
available from
Biblio Distribution Centre for
Sotheby Parke Bernet Publications,
81 Adams Drive,
Totowa, New Jersey 07512

First reprinted 1980

ISBN 0 85667 019 7

Designed by Paul Sharp
Set in Monophoto Ehrhardt by
Westerham Press
Printed in England by
Jolly & Barber Ltd, Rugby

Contents

Abbreviations used in the catalogue
c   circa
HM   Hallmark
[ ]   indicates that doubt exists

Fig 1
The armorial bearings of the Company

TEMPUS · RERUM · IMPERATOR

A brief account of the Worshipful Company of Clockmakers

The Origin of the City Guilds

The Worshipful Company of Clockmakers is one of the eighty-six remaining London Companies which are direct descendants from the medieval craft guilds whose original function was the control of the City's trade in the Middle Ages. The guild system was, indeed, an essential part of the medieval economic, social and political system throughout Western Europe. London is one of the few cities where vestiges of this system still survive, albeit with few of its former functions now operative.

How the guilds arose is a matter of speculation, for there is insufficient contemporary evidence from which to draw safe conclusions. Nevertheless, there are some grounds for believing that the Church played a significant role in their formation. The religious obligations that the medieval Church laid upon its members were far stronger than anything that we know today. Mutual support in poverty, sickness and misfortune; decent burial and masses for the souls of the departed; regular attendance at church on holy days; these were practical requirements for all men.

From the earliest times religious fraternities flourished, dedicated to particular saints in whose honour chapels were erected in local churches; these were the channels through which Man's religious duties were directed. Medieval London abounded in such religious fraternities and guilds. And since it was the custom of the various trades or crafts to group themselves in particular precincts of the City – as is evidenced by the survival of many street names, such as Bread Street, Goldsmith's Row, the Vintry – it is likely that religious guilds attending their local churches would be composed predominantly of members of particular trades. Each of the surviving pre-Reformation companies of London is designated in its charter as being a guild in honour of a saint, and it is significant that the saint's name always precedes that of the craft or trade, such as 'the guild or fraternity of the Blessed Mary of the Drapers of London'. Moreover, the earliest surviving ordinances (those of the Carpenters and the Saddlers) are concerned solely with the religious and fraternal duties of their members; secular affairs play no part in them.

If the foregoing hypothesis is acceptable, it is readily understood how a common interest of their members' calling would play an increasingly important part in the meetings of the various fraternities. And, although at the time of the Reformation, the survival of the guilds depended on their claim to be secular guilds, practical religion continued to play an important part in their activities, as, indeed, it still does in their recognition of fraternal obligations. Thus, around their religious duties and fraternal conviviality the early guilds developed their industrial supervision.

Signs of supervision of the crafts and trades of the City by their respective guilds appear as early as the twelfth century. The main facets of the control, as embodied later in charters and ordinances, were the regulation of the price of goods, the initiation of the earliest form of technical education through apprenticeship, and the inspection of products, backed by the right of search, so as to ensure a minimum standard of quality. Each guild limited the number of apprentices and forbad the conduct of its trade to any other than those who had been admitted to its freedom; only Freemen were citizens and only citizens could work. Such a system gave to the guilds a monopoly. Nevertheless, it protected the customer against poor quality goods, employers against bad workmen and workmen against bad employers. Some have seen in the early guilds the origin of the trade union but they were more of the nature of a combination of employers' federation, trade union and friendly society.

There seems little doubt that in the context of the economic system of the Middle Ages these guilds were beneficial. They reached their hey-day in the fifteenth and sixteenth centuries. Trade and municipal affairs were firmly in their hands. But it is paradoxical that the guilds' trade and craft control, when at its height, coincided with the beginnings of the guilds' decline as an economic force. The expansion of trade and the improved communications under the Tudors imposed a severe strain on an inflexible system which, generally, was opposed to expansion. Nevertheless, the guilds struggled for some time to impose their regulations upon an expanding economy. Indeed, the seventeenth century saw the formation of a number of new companies, and it was at this time that the Clockmakers' Guild was formed.

In the wording of the original charters various names were employed to describe the guilds, examples being 'fraternity', 'commonalty', 'society', or, in the case of the Clockmakers, 'fellowship', and gradually for convenience, a single collective term 'company' (meaning 'assembly') was adopted by the guilds as a common title, the sole exception being the Society of Apothecaries. In a similar way, there is no legal authority for the adoption of the word 'worshipful' now used as part of the descriptive style of the original guilds. It is strictly a courtesy title meaning dignified, proud or honourable and, exceptionally, it is this last designation that is used by the Honourable Company of Master Mariners, the title having been conferred on them by King George V at their inauguration in 1928.

By the end of the eighteenth century the guilds' original functions, although never legally rescinded in London, became with a few exceptions inoperative. A feature of English institutions is, however, their capacity to adapt to changing conditions. During the nineteenth century the corporate conscience asserted itself and the companies found a new life in promoting through charitable endeavours, general and technical education and in developing strong interests in their respective crafts. The progress of technology owes much to the practical encouragement given in recent times by the guilds, notably in the foundation of the City and Guilds of London Institute, as well as in numerous scholarships and institutes endowed throughout the country.

The origins of the Clockmakers' Company

[1] Astronomical clocks, made of wood and driven by water, existed in China as early as AD 725.
[2] Modern parlance tends to associate the work of the blacksmith with the shoeing of horses, but this was the role of the farrier; the blacksmith was an artist in iron.

From the earliest times man has invented devices for timekeeping, starting with the hour-glass and sundial, but the mechanical clock did not appear until the end of the thirteenth century[1]. At around 1600 clockmaking in England was still the work of blacksmiths[2] and confined to making large church or tower clocks and heavy chamber clocks from iron. Watchmaking seems to have originated in Europe in the early part of the sixteenth century, but it did not become a native craft in England until the end of the century. However, from about 1600 onwards, English artists soon rivalled the Continental masters in producing watches of increasing mechanical refinement and decorative appearance.

A document exists which shows that in 1622 there were sixteen clock and watch makers in London and that their work was beginning to be harmed by a 'multiplicitie of Forreniers using theire profession in London'. At this period 'foreigners' did not necessarily mean aliens, the term being used to designate all those living in the City and its suburbs who were not Freemen, whether English or from abroad. One source of craftsmen, from which the guilds faced competition since the seventeenth century, was the Protestant refugees from the Continent, and, from evidence listed in the 1622 petition, it seems that the intruders into the clockmaking trade were French Protestants, or Huguenots, who had sought refuge in England from religious persecution. These had succeeded in filling a new Continental demand for small, light and decorative watches and portable clocks, and had then arrived in England in numbers that exceeded those of their London counterparts. The Freemen clockmakers of the City had obtained their freedom to practice their craft mainly through the Blacksmiths' Company and, no doubt, the simplicity of the medieval iron clock allowed a specialist blacksmith to make one, but the complexity and fineness of the new small clocks and watches needed more delicate skills. No longer was it sufficient to be a worker in iron to produce a portable timekeeper, and those who practised the new craft had become, by the beginning of the seventeenth century, conscious of their separate identity.

As early as 1627 the clockmaker Freemen had induced the Blacksmiths' Company to oppose on their behalf the intrusion of the French clockmakers into the City. In the following year the clockmakers once more showed their solidarity by attempting to persuade the blacksmiths to give recognition to the craft by formally incorporating blacksmiths and clockmakers in a new charter. The blacksmiths did indeed obtain a new charter but denied the clockmakers the status they sought. Undeterred, the clockmakers petitioned the Crown for a charter of incorporation[3] of their own. This move was opposed by the blacksmiths: a natural reluctance to lose important sections of their craft was a feature of the guilds in the seventeenth century. Whereas the Middle Ages was a period of mergers, the seventeenth century began to exhibit the trend towards specialisation which is so prominent among crafts, professions and trades today. Both the needlemakers and the gunsmiths of the City, who, like the clockmakers, were in former times partly under the tutelage of the Blacksmiths' Company, found a similar opposition to their desire for self-rule.

Eventually, the clockmakers were successful, and their Charter was granted in the reign of King Charles I on 22 August 1631. It had the effect of giving the English workmen powers to control 'the horological trade in the City of London and within ten miles thereof, and incorporated a controlling body which should have continuance for ever under the style and name of the Master, Wardens and Fellowship of the Art or Mystery[4] of Clockmaking.' The Charter provided, further, that the Fellowship should be governed by one Master, three Wardens and ten or more Assistants who formed the Court of Assistants. The Charter also appointed the first Master and Wardens by name; these were:

Master   David Ramsay[5]
Wardens Henry Archer
            John Wellowe (Willow)
            Sampson Shelton
(The Charter also named ten Assistants)

The original Charter is still in the possession of the Company and is deposited in Guildhall Library where it may be seen by appointment.

Although the Clockmakers' Company had obtained their Charter it was still not obligatory for clock and watch makers to become Freemen of our Company. Many horological workmen were already free of other companies and, consequently, owed their allegiance to them, although the quality of their workmanship was supervised by the Clockmakers' Company. In order to improve this unsatisfactory state of affairs, the Clockmakers' Company, in 1697, petitioned the Lord Mayor and Aldermen for an Act which would require all apprentices working in the art of clock and watch making to take the Freedom of the Clockmakers' Company when their time expired. This application was actively opposed by the Blacksmiths' Company who appreciated that if the Act were passed it would further diminish the extent of their authority and that their revenue would also be affected.

[3] A charter of incorporation authorises a body to act as a legal person, hence the seal which is the equivalent of a signature.

[4] Mystery (or mistery): from the Latin *ministerium*, medieval Latin *misterium*, meaning occupation, craft. It has, here, no implications of secrecy.

[5] Alternative forms of spelling occurred frequently in these early days. Even State Papers refer to Ramsey, Ramsay or Ramsy but the name engraved on watches made by the first Master of the Company is Ramsay.

Plate II

Watch and chatelaine by Wightwick &
Moss, England c1806 *(catalogue number
287)*

Watch by John Ramsay, England or
Scotland c1625 *(catalogue number 12)*
Watch by Goullons, France c1650
(catalogue number 32)
Watch by Gray & Constable, England
c1790 *(catalogue number 232)*

Watch by Pierre Roumieu, France c1650
(catalogue number 31)
Watch by Milleret & Tissot, Switzerland
early 19th century *(catalogue number 364)*

Plate III
Watch by Christopher Egleton, England
c1700 *(catalogue number 116)*
Watch by James Grantham, England
c1750 *(catalogue number 183)*

Watch by Brockbanks, England 1812/13
(catalogue number 440)

Watch by Daniel Quare with enamel case
by Huaud, England c1712
(catalogue number 131)
Watch by Jean Hubert, France c1650
(catalogue number 30)

[6] It would seem that both Companies were agreed that 'great Church Clockmakers of Iron' were under the sole control of the Blacksmiths' Company.

In the dispute that then arose the Blacksmiths' Company contended that it was 'well knowne that they were the original and proper makers of clocks . . . and that no clockmaker can finish any clock without the distinct and peculiar workmanship of ye Smith . . .'. On the other hand, the Clockmakers' Company drew attention to their bye-laws, approved by Parliament in 1632, which stated that their Company was responsible for 'trading in clocks[6], watches, alarums, sun-dials, case making, graving and mathematical instrument making in any nature or material whatsoever . . .'. Unfortunately for the Clockmakers' Company the Lord Mayor and Aldermen decided in favour of the Blacksmiths' Company, and it was not until sixty-eight years later, in 1765, that the Clockmakers' Company was at last successful in obtaining an Act of Common Council which required that all those working at clockmaking should take the Freedom of our Company.

It has been mentioned that mathematical instrument-making was one of the specialised trades that had been allocated to the Clockmakers' Company at their inception, a branch of the Company's activities which was, in 1813, the cause of another dissension. This time it was with the Company of Spectacle Makers who, in a new armorial device, had included emblems connected with mathematical instruments and, once again, the Lord Mayor had to intervene.

Today, happily, these controversies are completely forgotten and they are interesting only as forming part of our history.

The Court of Assistants

The Court of Assistants comprising the Master, three Wardens and not less than ten Assistants, is the governing body of the Company. At present there are fourteen Assistants in addition to the Master and Wardens. The Wardens are known, respectively, as the Senior Warden, the Renter Warden, who is primarily responsible to the Court for the Company's finances, and the Junior Warden.

Assistants are elected to the Court from the Livery. On a vacancy arising, the Master invites his Wardens and Assistants to nominate Liverymen to fill the vacancy. Candidates, duly nominated, are elected to the office of Assistant by the Court on a show of hands, or, if a poll is demanded by any Assistant, on a ballot being taken. An Assistant, once elected, continues in office for life and cannot be removed save in exceptional circumstances. An Assistant may, however, be permitted by the Court to resign his office. It is the practice to refer to those Assistants who have served in the office of Master as Past Masters.

The Master and Wardens

The Master and Wardens are elected by the Court of Assistants from amongst their number. Election is on a show of hands and is, customarily, by seniority on the Court, but an Assistant is not considered eligible for election as a Warden until he has served on the Court for a minimum of three years. The office of Junior Warden is served first, then Renter Warden followed by Senior Warden, and, ultimately, the office of Master.

Freemen and Liverymen

Admission (membership) to the Company is by invitation and requires the sponsorship of a member of the Court. The first step is to be admitted (elected) a Freeman, and since 1715 women have been accepted to this class. Later, the Freeman can be invited to become a Liveryman, the latter title enabling the individual to take part in the official ceremonies of the Company.

Officers of the Company

The executive officer of the Company is the Clerk who is assisted in court ceremonial by the Beadle.

The office of the Honorary Librarian and Curator of the Company is held by the Librarian of Guildhall and he is assisted in horological matters by an Assistant Curator appointed by the Company.

The Master and his Court exercise their general supervision of the Museum and Library through the appointment of an Honorary Surveyor and an Assistant Honorary Surveyor, both of whom are members of the Court.

The individuals to hold the above appointments are nominated by the Court annually.

Armorial bearings

On 31 January 1671, armorial bearings were granted to the Company, the original parchment of which is preserved in Guildhall Library. In 1967, Mr Gerald Cobb, a herald painter at the College of Arms, was commissioned to re-draw our armorial bearings, and his final design is shown in Fig 1. The clock in the centre of the shield has been drawn exactly as described in the grant of 1671, and, although to the modern horological eye it has several peculiarities in decoration and style, it is, nevertheless, important as being one of the earliest proofs that twisted columns were in use on clocks at this early date. These columns can also be seen on the engraved brass plate (Fig 2) which is fixed to the outer cover of a book of regulations governing the conduct of the Company and which is dated 31 January 167½, ie 1672 by modern reckoning as in those days the calendar did not change until 25 March of the New Year.

The Company's motto is *Tempus rerum imperator*: Time is the ruler of all things. This motto has been symbolised in the armorial device by the supporters representing Father Time and a regal figure who is described in the wording of the original grant of arms as an 'Emperor robed, crowned and holding a sceptre'.

Fig 2
Engraved brass plate dated 31 January 1671/2 illustrating twisted pillars on a clock

Plate IV
Watch by Julien Le Roy, France c1740
(catalogue number 156)
Watch by Conyers Dunlop, England mid
18th century *(catalogue number 319)*

Watch by Benjamin Bell, England c1690
(catalogue number 63)

Watch by Soret, Switzerland 1812/13
(catalogue number 291)
Watch by Simon Decharmes, England
early 18th century *(catalogue number 78)*

Plate V

Astronomical clock by Johann Schneider,
Germany c1625 *(catalogue number 585)*
Marine watch by John Harrison & Son,
England 1770 *(catalogue number 598)*

Long-case clock by
Edward East,
England c1675
(catalogue number 544)

Long-case clock by
James Harrison,
England 1728
(catalogue number 553)

The Tompion Gold Medal

In 1954, the Company decided to commemorate any outstanding achievement in the world of horology by the award of a Gold Medal. This medal is awarded at the discretion of the Court, from time to time, but never more than once in any calendar year, and anyone in the world is eligible to receive it. The medal is known as the Tompion Gold Medal in memory of Thomas Tompion who is regarded as the 'Father of English clock and watch making' and who was Master of the Company in 1704.

The recipients of the Tompion Gold Medal are:

1954 Mr W.H. Shortt, for the invention in 1925 of the Shortt Free-pendulum clock which for the next thirty years was to remain the standard timekeeper at observatories throughout the world.

1955 Mr W.A. Marrison (USA), for work in the development of the Quartz-crystal clock.

1957 Dr Louis Essen, for his development of the Essen Ring Quartz-crystal oscillator, and of the first Atomic Clock of very high precision.

1963 Mr Max Hetzel (a Swiss citizen working in the USA), for his development of the tuning fork as a time standard for the wristwatch.

Library and Museum

Although the Company has never been wealthy enough to own its own hall, it is fortunate in possessing a large horological library and also a very important collection of clocks and watches. It was in 1813 that the Company founded a library of books and manuscripts connected with horology and, in 1816, it began to collect rare examples of clocks, watches and their mechanisms, watch-keys and other scientific items. In 1873, the entire collection was deposited on loan at Guildhall where it is in the custody of the Librarian of the Corporation of London, and the whole is open for view and study by the public.

The Library comprises more than 1500 books covering the whole history of horology, and included are the complete Court records of the Clockmakers' Company since its inception. Amongst the many literary rarities is the first printed book devoted to a clock, Micheli's *Della dichiaratione de l'horologio di Mantova*, 1547; Pietro Bembo's *Epistolae*, 1535, in which occurs the first recorded mention of an alarm clock; and the first book on clocks and watches to be printed in England, John Smith's *Horological dialogues*, 1675. Publications of more modern date have not been neglected and every effort is made to acquire currently published books of horological quality and this includes the maintenance of complete runs of important horological journals as well as collecting workshop data of interest to the practical clock and watch restorer.

Many of the manuscripts belonging to the Company are of great rarity, and mention must be made of the numerous original documents, drawings, essays and letters of John Harrison and his son, William, mostly in their own handwriting, concerning the Harrison timekeepers for determining the longitude of a ship at sea. The Company is also proud of its collection of portraits in oil and other media as well as engravings of some of the celebrated clock and watch makers of the past including T. Tompion, J. Harrison, T. Mudge, A. Cumming, Vulliamy and others. Finally, mention must be made of the large collection of over 1250 watch-papers, discs used by Georgian and Victorian watchmakers as a pad for insertion·between the watch and its outer protective case. These paper discs, in addition to being artistically engraved often with sentimental or monitory lines, were used also as advertisements and hence provide a valuable reference to makers of the past and their addresses.

J. B.
H. Q.
1975

Preface

The collection of clocks and watches belonging to the Worshipful Company of Clockmakers can claim with almost complete certainty to be the oldest collection in the world devoted solely to horology. It is not known at what exact date it started to be formed, but many acquisitions are recorded in the second decade of the nineteenth century. The Musée des Arts et Métiers in Paris, which dates from the French Revolution, has its highly important collection of marine timekeepers by Ferdinand Berthoud and the unique timekeeper of Pierre Le Roy; but this is a highly specialised group, forming a part only of the entire museum. The collection of the Clockmakers' Company is wide in its scope, although it is not so complete as the great Ilbert Collection, now housed in the British Museum, but, although its emphasis is more technical than decorative, it can claim nevertheless to be among the world's most comprehensive collections. In the half century when precision timekeeping was being developed, from about 1770 to 1820, it may claim to be without rival, both as to its watches and its marine chronometers.

Catalogues were previously published in 1875, 1902 and 1949. The last of these, prepared by that great horological historian G. H. Baillie, is now out of print and also considerably out of date because of the large number of additions to the collection since it was written. G. H. Baillie's catalogue, however, remains the basis of the present one. Considering the increase in historical knowledge since his day it is remarkable how seldom an entry of his has called for amendment or enlargement.

In the course of its long history it was inevitable that the collection should have come by a number of pieces which either are duplicates, or completely lacking in interest, or unworthy of mention. In order to keep the catalogue to a manageable size such pieces have been omitted. Even so, the catalogue lists many items of little interest individually but worthy of inclusion because they help to build up a complete chronological sequence. Not all of the catalogued items are on display but these are stored in Guildhall and may be seen by special arrangement.

To an extent the catalogue is critical; non-original features are pointed out and several watches purporting to be by famous makers are included because of their interest as forgeries and they are listed as such.

No precise format has been followed, the amount of detail being proportional to the interest of the exhibit. Exact dates are given where they are known, otherwise an attempt has been made to date objects within a decade. Where even this has not seemed advisable (notably in watch movements) expressions such as 'late eighteenth century' have been applied.

In preparing this catalogue, Baillie's system of numbering has not been retained mainly because the items have now been catalogued in three main categories: Watches, Clocks, Miscellaneous. These categories are then sub-divided into the specialist sections listed in the Contents. Each of these specialised sections has its own Introduction which provides a background of historical and technical information to the more important entries.

The 1949 catalogue described generally the type of numerals on dials, which can lead to a number of difficulties in cataloguing and may occupy a good deal of space to no great advantage. This information, therefore, has not been included in the present edition with one exception. Before 1800, in watches, it was almost universal to include minute numerals (usually at five-minute intervals). After 1800 they are found extremely rarely. Exceptions either side of this date-line are generally mentioned.

Donors are given under each catalogue entry. Where none is cited it is either because the method of acquisition is not known, or because the piece in question was acquired by purchase. Two very large additions to the collection have come to it as complete collections. These are referred to, respectively, as the 'Nelthropp Collection' and the 'Collinson Collection'. The former immense collection was given or bequeathed to the Company by the Rev H. L. Nelthropp, who was Master in 1893. The latter, which has filled many gaps in the collection, was presented in 1966 by Howard Arthur Collinson, a present Liveryman of the Company.

Throughout the catalogue every item has been individually numbered in sequence, but these numbers are, of course, only chronological within each specialised section. In four cases where a clock has been converted to a later form, ie from balance to pendulum, it comes under two sections and is therefore entered twice. The first of these entries relates to the clock in its present converted form and is only given a brief description, while the second entry relates to the clock in its original form and includes its main description. Each of these double entries is cross-referenced.

The Index includes the names of makers and, also, other names and specialised subjects mentioned in the text of the catalogue.

The collection has been lodged at Guildhall in the City of London since 1873, and the Company acknowledges gratefully its debt to the Corporation of London for housing the exhibits and for providing the many services which a museum open to the public demands.

The compilers of this catalogue wish to record their special thanks to Colonel H. Quill R.M., who, in his capacity as Honorary Surveyor of the Company's Collection for the past eight years, laid the foundations of this catalogue and gave his generous assistance throughout. They would also like to express their gratitude to Mr Cedric Jagger, the Assistant Curator to the Company, for his valuable assistance in checking the proofs and in indexing the catalogue.

The Librarian of the Corporation, Mr Godfrey Thompson, has accepted the position of Honorary Librarian and Curator to the Company, and the Company wishes to record its great appreciation of the care that he and his staff have devoted to the collection.

Cecil Clutton
Past Master

George Daniels
Court of Assistants
1975

4a

4b

4c

Watches

Watches with verge escapement

Of all the clocks and watches in the collection, it is not very surprising that almost half have the verge escapement. Every horological writer for the last two hundred years has been at pains to vilify it despite its having a production run of six centuries, which must surely be a record for any form of mechanism. The collection has examples of the verge escapement from the late fifteenth century up to 1860, and the earliest watch dates from about 1580. However, it is arguable that the two oldest items in the section devoted to spring-driven balance-wheel clocks (catalogue numbers 581 and 582) should be regarded as watches. Portable clocks small enough to be classified as watches go back into the fifteenth century although none survives from before about the middle of the sixteenth century. Popular at that time were small drum-shaped clocks, such as catalogue numbers 581 and 582, made in a wide range of sizes, of which the smallest certainly would not have been made so small if they were not intended to be regularly carried. This they could be, either in a small handbag, or in a bag suspended from a belt or round the neck. Catalogue number 581 is only 63mm in diameter, and it is only its depth of 38mm that prevents it being carried in a modern pocket. This clock may antedate by half a century the collection's oldest undeniable watch, catalogued in this section, the style of which places it early in the last quarter of the sixteenth century. It was about then that the sharp contours of the straight-sided and flat-topped drum clock began to be rounded. Of this type is catalogue number 1, of which the case is the best and most certainly authentic part. The works of sixteenth-century watches have understandably enough seldom survived in their original state; but this movement gives the impression of having been built up at a later date; possibly at the time when the balance spring was added. Nevertheless, it retains the earliest form of striking train and the profoundly unsatisfactory stackfreed. The plates are of brass, but the wheels are steel except for the escape-wheel. Thus, except for the brass escape-wheel, all the characteristics of the watch are German.

Only a little later, and basically similar, is catalogue number 4, which is illustrated. This also was converted at a very early date to balance-spring. Roughly contemporary is number 5, the earliest British watch in the collection, dating from the end of the reign of Elizabeth I, by Michael Nouwen.

English work in the first quarter of the seventeenth century is characterised particularly by an engraved border to the top plate of the movement, and this is well shown in the illustration of catalogue number 6, by Robert Grinkin, of about 1625. This watch retains the type of cock typical of the period, attached to the plate by having a rectangular slot in the cock foot which fits over a similarly-shaped peg fixed to the plate. Both peg and cock are drilled to receive a tapered pin driven through from side to side, which firmly locates the cock. Despite retaining this original cock the watch was converted to balance-spring, probably about 1680, since the spring is of very early type, having only $1\frac{1}{2}$ turns; and the regulator is of the early 'Barrow' type.

Grinkin was one of the first Freemen of the newly-formed Worshipful Company of Clockmakers in 1632, and its first Master was the very famous Scot, David Ramsay who is represented by catalogue numbers 7 and 19, which are illustrated. Number 19 has a typical early rock crystal case, but number 7 is a particularly splendid watch in the shape of a six-pointed star. The typically British engraved border follows the star-shaped outline of the movement plate. As is usual in British work of the period, the piercing and shape of the pegged-and-pinned cock has a strongly French flavour. Also typical is the ratchet wheel and spring-tensioned click by means of which the tensioning of the mainspring is adjusted, and which provides the only means of regulating the rate of the watch. This watch lay hidden for many years behind a tapestry at Gawdy Hall, Norfolk, and was discovered only at the end of the eighteenth century which no doubt accounts for its pristine state.

Catalogue number 8 is an anonymous piece, almost certainly French and probably a little earlier than Ramsay's number 7. The similarity of the cocks is apparent from the illustration. In both watches the movement is fixed to the case by two spring-tensioned clips, which are drawn together by the finger-nails to withdraw the movement.

German watchmaking almost completely faded out in the early seventeenth century owing to the disastrous economic effects of the Thirty Years War; however, the British and French styles became firmly established on the lines illustrated in these early pieces. From then on, until the introduction of the balance spring in about 1675, no technical advances took place, although tooth-cutting, especially that of pinions, gradually improved. The ingenuity of watchmakers was therefore channelled into the visually attractive but technically uninteresting pursuit of complicated calendar work, and decorated cases. Metal cases were made in the shape of various objects such as crosses, birds or skulls. Cases of rock crystal were popular up to about 1650 when painting on enamel began to be used for watch cases and dials and remained popular, in varying degree, for nearly two hundred years. All these forms of decoration are well represented in the collection and are illustrated. Catalogue number 36, by James Nellson, of about 1660, which is illustrated, is a good example of the multiple calendar dial.

Pegged-and-pinned cocks began to give way to screwed-on cocks about the middle of the century, and the traditional British engraved border to the movement disappeared. This gave room on the plate to introduce the more precise worm-and-wheel set-up regulator, and all these trends are exemplified in the illustration of catalogue number 28, by Benjamin Hill, of about 1650.

Concurrently with increasingly decorative watch cases from France, the puritanical trends at home produced some of the most elegantly simple watches of any period. The watch, quite devoid of decoration and of elongated oval shape, was protected by an equally plain outer case. The dial was protected by the precursor of the modern watch-glass which (in the earliest specimens) was of crystal, fitted into a ring screwed to the bezel. Only the movement retained its traditional decoration. These watches, known as 'Puritan watches' are nearly always of silver, although there is one of gold in the Ashmolean Museum, Oxford. A fine example, catalogue number 22, by the most famous of all pre-balance-spring watchmakers, Edward East, is illustrated.

Edward East had an immensely long life and while the dates of his birth and death are not known with certainty, the indications are that he lived from 1602 to 1697. He was one of the ten original Assistants on the Court of the Clockmakers' Company in 1632 and clocks and watches bearing his name continue almost up to the end of his life, when he seems to have had no successor. He was Master in 1645 and 1652, and in 1693 he gave to the Company £100 'now in his life-time'. East's work is remembered mostly by his early watches and travelling clocks, especially in the years when he was Clockmaker to Charles I, and many of these survive in this collection and elsewhere. They are characterised particularly by the superbly elegant signatures in tall, rather stiff script lettering. Equally, the accuracy of his wheel-cutting shows that East did not earn his unrivalled reputation without good cause. He was one of the first makers to take up the newly-invented pendulum in the early 1660s, but by the time the balance-spring

48a

48b

48c

for watches appeared he was already over seventy and probably taking only a nominal part in the business. One or two balance-spring watches bearing his name exist of which an early example (catalogue number 46) is illustrated. This is interesting in possessing all the characteristics of the earliest balance-spring movements. The pierced cock foot has an irregular border and at the point where the table joins the foot there is no engraved mask, such as became universal by 1690. The regulator is of the wheel and sector type said to have been introduced by Tompion.

It is with the name of Thomas Tompion that the early balance-spring experiments in England are associated; curiously, although otherwise unconnected, he and East were born within a few miles of each other in Bedfordshire. Tompion was born in 1639 and after East's ascendancy his became the foremost name for the rest of the century.

The story of the invention of the balance-spring and all the hard swearing and vituperation that surrounded it is well known, as is Tompion's association in experimental work with Robert Hooke. He was only in his mid-thirties at the time (1675) and recently set up in London, where he was accepted into the Clockmakers' Company in 1671. The Company is fortunate, therefore, in possessing not only one of his first balance-spring watches (catalogue number 48, illustrated) which has a later dial, but also his only recorded watch without a balance-spring. This has survived only as a movement without a dial but there is a typical worm-and-wheel set-up regulator. This very important piece is catalogue number 39 in the Collection and is illustrated. It must date from between 1671 and 1675.

With the invention of the balance-spring the accuracy of watches immediately narrowed from the almost unpredictable to within a couple of minutes a day. From what had been little more than a status symbol grew an instrument of practical utility. Immediately its decorative trappings fell away, and most of the early balance-spring watches are contained in plain pair-cases of silver or gold. Technical interest also revived as is apparent in the vigorous finish displayed in the fifteen years from 1675 to 1690 when makers were mastering the new technique.

With the new accuracy of performance it became significant to record minutes as well as hours. In the early days, several different methods of doing this were devised, and the resultant variety of dials is one of the most attractive features of the last quarter of the seventeenth century. There are four main types of which the 'sun-and-moon' dial is the most common and least important. An example, catalogue number 65, is illustrated. The only real interest of this rather naïve arrangement is that the lower half of the dial, which would otherwise be unoccupied, was frequently filled by the earliest seconds dials as in the example illustrated.

A more serious version consisting of a revolving plate seen through a cut-out space in the dial plate is the 'wandering-hour' dial. In this arrangement the hour appears through a window in a semi-circular slit in the dial plate. The dial plate has the minutes from 0–60 engraved round the edge of the slit and the hour window moves round the slit pointing to the minutes as it passes. As it reaches 60 another window and the next hour appear at 0. Thus, one glance established both the hour and minute. In the illustrated example (catalogue number 55) by G.D. Sinclare, the time is 6.22. For some reason, at present unknown, these 'wandering-hour' watches nearly always had some royal attribution (either a portrait of the reigning monarch or the royal arms) on the dial or movement. This watch is a rare exception to the rule.

The third and exceedingly rare arrangement is the 'differential dial', of which catalogue number 120, by Bushman, is illustrated. The minute hand behaves normally. In the centre of the dial is a small revolving circular plate with the hours engraved upon it. This plate revolves at eleven-twelfths the speed of the minute hand, so that the relevant hour is always under the minute hand. In the illustration the time (like the 'wandering-hour' dial just described) is again 6.22.

The fourth group tackles the problem in a quite different way. The dial is divided into only six hours, so that the single hand goes round twice in twelve hours. The dial is then engraved with I–VI in Roman numerals, and 7–12 in Arabic numerals. The Arabic 7 is over the Roman I; 8 over II and so on; so that to read the time one must first of all know which of the two alternative hours it is. The object of the arrangement was to give such a wide space between each pair of hours that the minutes could be engraved in two-minute units; so that the time could be read within a minute by a single hand. It is an elegant arrangement, but one which makes it difficult to tell the time without constant practice. In the example illustrated, catalogue number 50, by W. Bertram, the time is either 4.23 or 10.23.

Yet another arrangement was used by Richard Street, but as far as is known by no one else. He employed what look like ordinary hour and minute hands; but the minute hand goes round in only fifteen minutes. Each minute division has six subdivisions of 10 seconds each, so that the time can be read to within a few seconds. Street, who is known to have worked for Sir Isaac Newton, also made a long-case clock with the same arrangement which is now in the Octagon Room in the old Greenwich Observatory. He almost certainly made these clocks and watches for observation use. The watch, catalogue number 102, has an equation of time scale engraved on the back and the movement is of the highest quality, with what is thought to be the earliest surviving example of a reversed fusee.

Despite all these experimental dials, the finally accepted separate hour and minute hands had established themselves by about 1680; but the survival for a further twenty or thirty years of the variants shows how difficult many people found it to read the time instinctively from two hands. Very occasionally, an early two-handed watch had also a seconds hand in the now usual place at 6 o'clock and perhaps the finest surviving example, both as to execution and condition is catalogue number 63, by Benjamin Bell. This characteristic type of champlevé dial with a matt centre is commonly found, both in silver and gold, but the silver ones have usually become black with age and misguided efforts to polish them. However, the matt portions were originally finished almost white (by a form of heat treatment) and in this example by Bell this dazzling finish is seen at its best.

Hands at this time, almost without exception, were of one of two patterns: the 'beetle and poker' or 'tulip and pointer'. The Benjamin Bell is an example of the latter, the similarity of the hour hand to a tulip flower being obvious. The accompanying hand was invariably a plain pointer. More usual but less elegant was the 'beetle and poker' of which an example is catalogue number 78, a watch with a gold champlevé dial by Simon Decharmes. The hour hand is said to resemble the wings of a stag-beetle, while the shaped minute hand is like a poker.

Most watches of the period have pair-cases. To wind the watch the outer case has to be removed to expose the winding hole in the back of the inner case. This not only made the watch thicker than was practically necessary, but wasted a significant amount of metal, especially if it was gold. Quare sometimes overcame this disability by bringing the winding square through the dial and so could employ only a single case. He then had to make a heavily cranked and rather ugly minute hand to avoid the winding square and he also provided for regulating the watch through the dial, so that the owner need never have access to the works. An example with a gold dial is catalogue number 126, illustrated; but although the fine gold case fits the movement perfectly, it is not only a conventional pair-case, but hallmarked 1728, long after Quare was dead. Such anomalies as these are not infrequent among old watches and often no obvious reason for them can be discovered. By its serial number (3720) the date of the movement must be about 1710 and it is thus one of the earliest watches to employ jewelling, which was developed by Nicholas Facio in 1704. The large, faceted diamond endstone, shown in the illustration, is typical of early jewelling as used by Quare, Graham and a few others.

In the meantime the French had developed a form of watch dial similar to their clocks, with brass dial plates and porcelain hour plaques attached to them. They had invariably single cases (commonly of brass-gilt; hardly ever of gold or at any rate only the smallest handful has survived) with winding through a hole in the dial. When there was only one hand (which the French continued to use until well after 1700) the winding square was usually in the centre of the boss of the hour hand, an arrangement to which Breguet reverted a century later for his *montres à souscription*. An example by Martinot, of about 1700, is illustrated, catalogue number 108. The movement of this watch, also illustrated, has a curious layout, found more commonly in French than in British watches of the time, mostly about the turn of the century. The clock pendulum was enough of a novelty for the superiority of its timekeeping still to be measured against the old, unsprung balance-wheel. So to make their watch balance-wheels look like a pendulum those makers who affected the arrangement allowed only half the wheel, and one spoke of it, to be seen, on which they mounted a blob of metal like a pendulum bob.

If French watches did not have a brass-gilt case, usually chiselled and engraved in small, intricate arabesque patterns, they had cases of painted enamel and the artists most frequently employed were the members of the Huaud family of Geneva. Very occasionally their work is found decorating an English watch, for example, catalogue number 131, by Daniel Quare, of about 1712. The case is signed *Les Frères Huaud*.

But in England, the outer cases at the turn of the century were plain gold or silver, or leather or tortoiseshell decorated with a pattern of gold or silver pins. Catalogue number 116 (illustrated) is a good example of tortoiseshell and silver pins, of about 1700, by Christopher Egleton. It was very much later that the practice of engine-turning cases became fashionable; thus catalogue number 121 (illustrated), a gold watch by Charles Gretton, hallmarked for 1702, which seems to be engine-turned, could present a serious stylistic problem. But close examination shows that it has been punched over a former in a radiating pattern which looks remarkably like barleycorn engine-turning.

By 1700 the technique of the balance-spring had been mastered insofar as it was going to be mastered for another three quarters of a century. As watch-making settled down once more to monotonous repetition it was inevitable that interest in decoration should again come to the fore, and the form it took predominantly was the ancient technique of metal repoussé. This had been applied to watches very occasionally in the seventeenth century (there is a specimen of about 1635 in the British Museum) but it did not begin to come into fashion in any general way until after 1715. It then continued in high fashion for the next fifty years, becoming increasingly coarse and exaggerated as time went on. But early examples may be very artistic and the collection possesses one such superlative gold case of about 1720, containing a movement by Windmills, which has the added merit of being in almost mint condition. This is illustrated in catalogue number 133.

After 1700, the verge escapement had few surprises in store, but it showed its stamina by continuing in large-scale production, even in really high-quality movements, throughout the first quarter of the nineteenth century. However, watches of the highest quality for the half-century from 1725–75 had the cylinder escapement and most of these, predictably, were in perfectly plain gold or silver cases.

After about 1820 the verge escapement lost ground to the cheap, slim, cylinder escapement watches which began to flood out of Switzerland. Nevertheless, fine, robust verge watches in silver pair-cases with coarsely pierced balance cocks in the old tradition, continued to be popular – particularly, it seems, with farmers, judging by the numbers which have survived with ploughing scenes painted in the centre of their enamel dials. The escapement continued to be made until after 1900 but the most recent in the collection (catalogue number 313) is an anonymous silver pair-case hallmarked 1860. Only six years older is another anonymous watch (number 311) which has engraved round the circumference of the dial plate 'Keep me clean and use me well and I to you the truth will tell'.

But despite this long, slow decline, three of the most important watches in the whole collection have verge escapements and date from after 1750. Of these, the collection's most prized possession, John Harrison's marine timekeeper H.5* (catalogue number 598), is described in the section devoted to Marine timekeepers. But catalogue numbers 187 and 189 are watches of the highest technical interest.

When John Harrison began to consider an alternative to his large marine timekeepers, of which he had made three (all in the National Maritime Museum at Greenwich) he turned to an almost completely new design in the shape of a very large watch. He made two of these, of which the collection has the second (H.5). The first (H.4) is also at Greenwich, and is the instrument with which he competed successfully for the £20,000 prize under the Act of 1714, for 'discovering the longitude'. But first he tried out his intended principles in a pocket watch, and since he had never undertaken fine watch work he employed a highly skilled watchmaker John Jefferys to work with him. Their prototype watch (catalogue number 187) has all but one of the refinements to be included in the triumphant H.4, just twice its size. These comprise maintaining power (to keep the watch going while it was being wound); temperature compensation; and diamond verge pallets of a highly sophisticated contour. Not one of these features had ever been used in a watch before.

The special quality of the diamond pallets is that they are set parallel to each other, instead of at an angle of about 100°, as is usual in verge watches, and they have curved backs which play an important part in the action of the escapement. The temperature compensation, like H.4 and 5, is a long bi-metallic strip acting upon the balance-spring; and the maintaining power is Harrison's own pattern which has continued in use in all good timekeepers containing a fusee. It is also

*For ease of reference the abbreviations H.1, H.2, H.3, H.4, and H.5, first coined by Commander R.T. Gould, are used throughout this catalogue when describing John Harrison's five longitude timekeepers.

lavishly jewelled to an extent unprecedented at the date, or for twenty years afterwards.

When it was finished Harrison, with characteristic generosity, allowed Jefferys to sign it – 'John Jefferys. London' on the back plate and 'John Jefferys. London. AD 1753' on the dust-cap. The hallmark on the silver pair-case is also for the year 1752–3.

Although these particulars of the watch were well known, the watch disappeared for many years and its rediscovery is due solely to Colonel H. Quill, RM. John Harrison used it as his personal pocket watch throughout his life, and it seems to have remained in the family until about 1905 when it was bought by Mr Rust of Messrs Barnby & Rust, jewellers, of 27 Silver Street, Hull. The watch was turned over to Mr R. S. Cochrane when he succeeded Mr Rust, together with a picture of Harrison and an unspecified book. In May 1941 the jeweller's shop was destroyed by bombs and the safe containing the watch was 'buried in heat for ten days'. Subsequently the watch, in a pitifully derelict condition, was donated to Hull Trinity House, but its significance was not appreciated. Providentially, after a long search, Colonel Quill found it there, in a drawer, in 1956, and offered to restore it. This he did, in co-operation with Mr David Evans, and the work was finally completed in 1964. The Lord Mayor of London at the time, Sir James Harman, who was also Master of the Clockmakers' Company, thereupon appealed to the Master Warden of Hull Trinity House who generously agreed to present the watch to the Company's Collection. It is illustrated, catalogue number 187, and the fierceness of the heat to which it has been subjected may be judged by the colour of the enamel dial which has changed from white almost to black. This is incapable of restoration, but it is an indication of the state to which the rest of the watch had been reduced and the truly wonderful skill and patience which has been devoted to its restoration.

Smaller and even more intricate is a watch of only two years later by Thomas Mudge, which has survived only as a movement now contained in a plain brass canister box (catalogue number 189, illustrated). It has been owned by the Company since 1850 when it was presented by John Grant, son of the famous watchmaker of the same name. What happened to the case is not known, but the tradition is that the watch was made for, and sold to, the King of Spain in 1755. It has an ordinary verge escapement and a balance-spring of five turns, on which acts a long bi-metallic regulator strip made up into a coil of six turns, the first time this very difficult feat had been accomplished. The watch does not have, or need, maintaining power since it has a complex and delicate remontoir which supplies power to the escapement and itself is wound by the train once a minute. In addition to this the train has an ordinary fusee. To achieve all this in a movement only 48mm in diameter was an achievement worthy of Mudge. It is interesting that he should have applied the verge escapement to a watch so intricate and sophisticated, rather than the reputedly superior cylinder, of which his training with George Graham had made him perfectly the master. It suggests that he had doubts as to the real superiority of the cylinder over the verge.

Verge escapement without balance-spring

1 Anonymous Germany c1580
Circular case. Back, edge and cover chased and chiselled. Back and cover sharply domed, edge curved. New pendant and hand. Silvered dial with engraved centre. Striking train. The balance, with later balance-spring and cock are c1700. Stackfreed and wheel missing. Wheels are steel except escape-wheel which is probably c1700. Brass plates. No spring barrels. Early form of striking. Hebrew letters A.L.Z.K. very small under top plate (a rather suspicious piece, probably with a built-up movement, but in a correct case).
Diam 70mm
Nelthropp Collection

2 Anonymous Germany c1600
Long octagonal case, gilt. Small cover with rectangular slots. Silver dial. Balance-wheel with large S cock. Double-pin regulator. Stackfreed. No spring barrel.
Length 45mm

3 Anonymous Germany c1600
Circular case, gilt. Flat edge, domed back and cover, all pierced and chiselled. Gilt dial with central sun. Steel hand. Balance-cock and count wheel are later replacements. Brass wheels and barrels. Top plate with engraved edge.

Three-wheel train. Later striking mechanism.
Diam 53mm
Nelthropp Collection

4 Anonymous Germany c1600
Circular case, re-gilded. Edge sharply curved, back and covers domed. All pierced and chiselled. Pendant replaced. Gilt 24-hour dial (I–XII Roman, 13–24 Arabic) with central sun. Hand replaced. Later balance with balance-spring. Later cock. Stackfreed spring replaced. Brass plates with steel wheels. No spring barrels. Early form of striking.
Diam 63mm
Nelthropp Collection
See illustration facing page 1

5 Michael Nouwen England c1600
Circular case, gilt. Edge and back pierced and chiselled. Cover appears to have been cut out and rim for snapped-in glass attached. Gilt dial with raised hour circle having figures of gold in dark blue enamel. Outer border of engraved foliate design. Centre engraved with rabbits and foliage. Hand missing. New piece of cock soldered on to table of original cock, which is pinned on. Steel balance. Four-wheel train. Later form of striking. Worm-and-

wheel set-up regulator, wheel replaced. Name engraved on plate round balance.
Diam 38mm
See also page 1
Nelthropp Collection

6 Robert Grinkin England c1625
Oval case, gilt and engraved. Gilt dial latched to top plate. The movement has a pinned-on cock and the back plate has an engraved border. Signed R Grinkin. The balance-spring of $1\frac{1}{2}$ turns and Barrow-type regulator were added probably in the late seventeenth century. Robert Grinkin of Fleet Street was a Freeman of the Blacksmiths' Company but became one of the first Freemen of the Clockmakers' Company at its formation in 1632. He served as Master in 1648, 1649 and 1654.
Length 59mm
See also page 1

7 David Ramsay Scotland c1625
Silver case, star-shaped with six points. Engraved all over including inside the covers, with biblical scenes. Silver dial with engraved centre, while the six points of the star have representations of angels of which that above XII holds a shield bearing the legend 'de Heck Sculp'. This signature by an engraver is unique and he was probably Gérard de Heck of Blois who was active from 1608–29.

6a

6b

6c

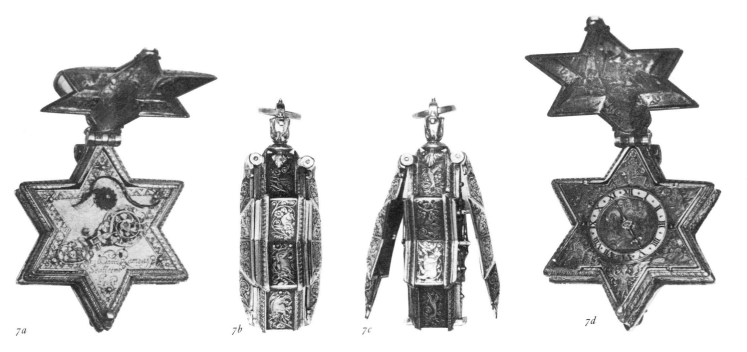

7a   *7b*   *7c*   *7d*

The movement has a pinned-on cock and ratchet set-up regulator. The top plate has an engraved border and is signed 'David Ramsay, Scotus me fecit'.

David Ramsay was the first Master of the Worshipful Company of Clockmakers at its formation in 1632. He was a Scotsman who was watchmaker to King James VI of Scotland, later (1603) King James I of England.

According to the *Norfolk and Norwich Archaeological Society Journal* Vol VI of 1864, pp 1–2, the watch was discovered c1790 secreted in a recess behind tapestry at Gawdy Hall near Harleston, Norfolk (subsequently demolished), with some apostle spoons.

Maximum diam 45mm

8 Anonymous [France] c1610
Elongated octagonal crystal case. Hinged crystal covers in engraved gilt frames.

Small pendant knob and finial. Gilt oval dial with engraved centre. Steel hand, tail broken. Narrow, oval, pinned-on cock. Four-wheel train. Ratchet set-up regulator. The fusee was cut for gut-line but a chain was fitted at a later date.

Length 37mm

Presented by 'Mr Auld of Edinboro', 1825. (Probably William Auld, partner in the well-known firm of Reid & Auld.)

9 Auguier France c1625
Oval silver case. Engraved edge-band. Front and back covers gilt. Movement hinged in the case. Gilt dial plate with small silver hour ring. Plate engraved with flowers and foliage. Steel hand with short tail. Movement with three-wheel train, and ratchet set-up regulator with pierced gilt cover. Cock with oval table, pinned on. Signed 'Auguier A nogent le Roi'.

Length 45mm
Presented by Charles Thistleton, 1830

10 Robert Grebauval France c1625
Long octagonal silver case. Hinged covers and movement. Sides engraved with foliage and animals. Back engraved with biblical scene. Front cover has a circular glass. Engraving of arms of Papillon, Kent, inside cover. Pendant replaced.

Gilt dial with small applied hour ring and engraved centre. Steel hand with long tail. Movement with fusee and gut-line. Three-wheel train. Ratchet set-up regulator with cover missing. Signed 'Robert Grebauval A Rouen'.

45 × 33mm

8a   *8b*   *8c*

11 **M.Z.**   Germany c1625
Oval case, silver-gilt. Flat edge-band engraved with flowers and foliage. Fixed gilt back with small central engraved pattern. Hinged bezel with rebate for glass. Cast pendant with hole pierced back to front. Silver dial. Engraved hour ring below, hand missing. Large age of moon circle above, steel hand with tail. Small dial on left for days of week with signs of planets. Moon-phase aperture on right with gilt moon and immediately above it a day-of-month aperture.
Three-wheel train. Oval screwed-on cock. Ratchet set-up regulator, part of click and cover missing. Later fusee and chain. Top plate signed in a cartouche 'M.Z.' (possibly Martinus Zoller of Augsburg).
This watch has been heavily restored.
Length 53mm

12 **John Ramsay**   England or Scotland c1625
Faceted oval rock crystal case; the crystal set in a metal frame enamelled white and green. There is a protective outer case of gilt metal. The dial is white enamel cloisonné with flowers. Gold chapter ring and blued steel hand.
The movement is signed 'John Ramsay fecit'. Nothing is known about this maker but two of the name are listed by G.H. Baillie who nevertheless says they may be the same man, active in Dundee 1610–46. Screwed-on balance-cock. Crystal case.
Length 38mm
See also colour plate II

13 **Richard Masterson**   England c1630
Silver oval case. Engraved flat edge-band. Plain back. Cover with crystal fixed by a ring. Cast pendant. Gilt dial plate engraved with cherubs and foliage. Silver hour ring with architectural scene engraved inside. Steel hand with long tail. Three-wheel train. Small long oval cock. Ratchet set-up regulator. Engraved border to back plate. Signed 'Ri. Masterson fecit'.
Masterson was a subscriber for the incorporation of the Clockmakers' Company in 1633, Master in 1642, died 1653.
Length 40mm
Nelthropp Collection

14 **Richard Masterson**   England c1630
Oval cast case in silver in the form of a cockle-shell. Winding hole with shutter.

Cast pendant, no finial. Silver dial with small engraved hour circle. Hand probably replaced.
Three-wheel train. Ratchet set-up regulator. Cock with oval table, pinned on. Engraved border to back plate. Signed 'Ri Masterson at the Exchange Fecit'. For Masterson's connection with the Clockmakers' Company. See 13 above.
Length 38mm

14a

14b

14c

15 **John Nicasius**   England c1630
Long octagonal crystal case and cover, the crystals set in gilt frames engraved with flowers and leaf pattern. Pendant and finial.
Gilt dial plate, engraved with flowers and foliage. Small silver hour ring. Steel hand with long tail.
Three-wheel train. Foot of pinned-on cock broken. The table almost covers the balance. Ratchet set-up regulator. Signed 'Nicasius Londini'.
Nicasius was an original member of the Clockmakers' Company in 1632 and Master in 1653.
Length 35mm

15a

15b

16 Edmund Bull England c1630
Oval silver pair-case, egg-shaped,
undecorated. Inner crystal cover. Silver
dial, plain with small chapter ring. Hand
missing. Silver cock, not original.
Ratchet set-up missing. Signed
'Edmund Bull in Fleet Street Fecit'.
Length 38mm

17 James Vautrollier England
c1630
Circular rounded silver case, undecorated.
Crystal held in cover by a ring. Silver dial
plate, plain with raised chapter ring with
touch-pins. Steel hand with long tail.
Three-wheel train. Ratchet set-up
regulator with steel tracery. Cock with
oval table and foot.
Signed 'James Vautrollier fecit'.
Vautrollier was known to be working in
1622 and was one of the first Assistants of
the Clockmakers' Company on its
incorporation.
Diam 40mm
Nelthropp Collection

18 A. Senebier Switzerland c1630
Crystal 8-lobed oval case with gilt
engraved rim.
Outer case of wood covered with fish-skin.
Gilt dial plate engraved with flowers.
Silver disc with chapter ring and an
engraved scene. Steel hand with long tail.
Ratchet set-up regulator with pierced gilt
cover and screw. Small pinned-on cock
with a rectangular foot.
Signed 'A. Senebier A Geneue'.
Attached is a small enamel plaque with
portrait of Charles I and on the back,
between a crown and a skull 'C.R.
Jan. 30. 1648'. Also a crystal locket
with very fair hair and a gold lyre charm.
Length 25mm

17a *17b*

17c

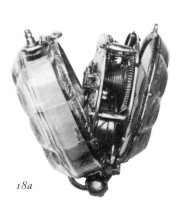

18a *18b* *18c*

19a *19b*

19 David Ramsay Scotland c1630
Octagonal rock crystal case, gold-mounted.
Gilt dial with an engraved scene, foliage
and animals. Pinned-on cock. Signed
'David Ramsay, Scotus me fecit'.
For particulars of David Ramsay see
number 7.
Length 23mm
Presented by Timex Watches, 1961

20 Henry Archer England c1630
Oval, metal-gilt case with silver covers and
a silver engraved band.
Silver dial, the centre engraved with a
scene and engraved gilt surround to the
chapter ring. Steel hand. Three-wheel
train. Oval pinned-on cock. Worm-and-
wheel set-up regulator. The back plate has
an engraved border.
Signed 'Henry Archer'.
Archer was the first Deputy Master of the
Clockmakers' Company and a Warden.
Length 63mm

21 Richard Crayle England c1630
Octagonal rock crystal case with gilt
mounts. Oval gilt 24-hour dial with
central engraved scene. Steel hand.
Oval cock. Worm-and-wheel set-up
regulator. Three-wheel train.
Signed 'Richard Crayle fecit'.
Length 63mm

22 Edward East England c1630
Oval silver undecorated pair-case. Outer
case of box form with a hook. Inner case
rounded. Crystal in cover fixed by a ring.
Silver dial with engraved chapter ring.
Steel hand with a long tail. Three-wheel
train. Ratchet set-up regulator. Pinned-on
cock with narrow oval table.
Signed 'Eduardus East Londini'.
East was an original member of the
Clockmakers' Company and Master in
1645 and 1652. He was watchmaker to
Charles I.

Outer case length 38mm
Inner case length 35mm
See also page 2
Nelthropp Collection

23 Edward East England c1640
Silver oval, egg-shaped, undecorated case.
Hinged cover with circular crystal held in
place by a ring with screws. Winding hole
with shutter. Silver dial with small
engraved chapter ring. Steel hand with
long tail.
Three-wheel train. Worm-and-wheel
set-up regulator. The balance has a
broad steel rim. Balance-cock with oval
table is located on a peg, but screwed to the
plate. Signed 'Eduardus East Londini'
(see 22 above).
Length 36mm

24 F. Sermand France or Switzerland
c1640
Silver case cast in the form of a tulip with
three crystal windows. Gilt dial plate with
large silver chapter ring. Floral engraving
outside the chapter ring and a scene inside.
Steel hand, long tail.
Three-wheel train. Ratchet set-up
regulator. Oval pinned-on balance-cock
with oval table. Signed 'F. Sermand'.
Length 33mm
Nelthropp Collection

25 William Clay England c1640
Silver-gilt case cast in the pattern of a
Tudor rose, which is continued onto the
bezel. Crystal missing.
Silver-gilt dial with engraved floral centre.
Hand replaced.

22a *22b* *22c*

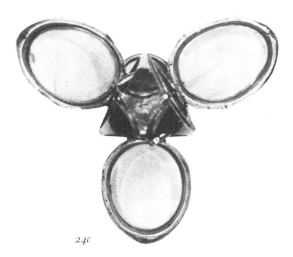

24a   *24b*   *24c*

Three-wheel train. Worm-and-wheel set-up regulator (wheel missing). Pinned-on cock. A balance-spring of only one turn, with no regulator, was added at a very early date and the balance-cock raised to accommodate the new balance and spring.
Signed 'William Clay, London'.
Clay was a Freeman of the Clockmakers' Company but his date of admission is not known.
Diam 32mm

26 Edward East England c1650
Movement only. No dial or hands. Pinned-on cock with narrow oval table. Worm and wheel set-up regulator. Three-wheel train with five-leaf pinions throughout.
Signed 'Eduardus East Londoni'.
Diam 38mm
Presented by B.L. Vulliamy, 1816

27 Francis Torado England c1650
Silver egg-shaped undecorated case. Silver dial with large chapter ring and touch pins. Steel hand with long tail. Three-wheel train. Worm-and-wheel set-up regulator. Pinned-on cock with a small table.
Signed 'Francis Torado in Gray's in'.
Torado was a Freeman of the Clockmakers' Company in 1633 and died in 1683.
Length 45mm
Presented by William Plumley, 1816

28 Benjamin Hill England c1650
Silver cast case in the form of a pomegranate with knob and ring pendant. The dial opening seems to have been cut out much later. Silver dial with sunk matt centre with engraved leaf pattern in centre. Steel hand with long tail. Three-wheel train. Worm-and-wheel set-up regulator with silver dial and steel tracery. Long oval screwed-on cock.
Signed 'Beniamin Hill Londini'.
Hill was a Freeman of the Clockmakers' Company in 1640, Master in 1657 and died 1670.
Diam 43mm
Nelthropp Collection

28a

25a   *25b*   *28b*

29 Edward East England c1650
Oval gold case. Gold dial with red and blue champlevé enamel; replacement.
Signed 'Eduardus East Londini'.
Length 32mm
Presented by G.S. Sanders, 1964

30 Jean Hubert France c1650
Metal-gilt case engraved with flower pattern on back and bezel. Knob and ring pendant. Dial with white enamel chapter ring surrounding an enamel portrait said to be Anne Marie Louise d'Orléans, Duchesse de Montpensier, born 1627. Hand replacement.
Three-wheel train. Worm-and-wheel set-up regulator. Cock with oval foot and nearly circular table.
Signed 'Jean Hubert A Rouen'.
Hubert was *Maître* in 1645 and *Juré* in 1664.
Diam 42mm
Nelthropp Collection
See also colour plate III

31 Pierre Roumieu France c1650
Rounded case with painted enamel scene of Mars and Venus. Blue enamel edge with panels of architectural scenes and a harbour scene painted on enamel inside the case. Plain gilt bezel with snap-in glass. The enamelled case is perhaps of a later date than the movement. White enamel dial on gilt plate. Steel hand with long tail.
Three-wheel train. Worm-and-wheel set-up regulator. Cock with long oval foot and nearly circular table.
Signed 'P. Roumieu. Rouen'.
Roumieu became *Maître* in 1645.
Diam 37mm
Nelthropp Collection
See also colour plate II

32 Goullons France c1650
Gold case, enamelled on back, edge, bezel and pendant loop with white flowers and foliage in relief and with black markings. Dial of white enamel with the centre decorated similarly as the case. Steel hand with short tail.
Three-wheel train. Worm-and-wheel set-up regulator. Cock nearly covering the balance. Signed 'Goullons A Paris'.
Diam 31mm
See also colour plate II

33 Estienne Hubert France c1650
Movement only. No dial. Three-wheel train. Worm-and-wheel set-up regulator. Cock with long oval foot and table nearly covering the balance.
Signed 'Estienne Hubert A Rouen'.
Diam 48mm
Presented by G. Atkins, 1818

34 Thomas Taylor England 1658
Silver pair-case. Outer case covered with leather studded with silver. Inner case engraved with a crown and 16–58. Above this is engraved 'OLIVAR' which may be original and below 'TO JOHN MILTON' which certainly is not. Glass in split bezel. Gilt dial with silver day-of-month ring and a gilt turning ring and pointer. Silver chapter ring with matt gilt centre. Very short steel hand with tail of nearly equal length.
Three-wheel train. Worm-and-wheel set-up regulator, with steel tracery. Wheel replaced. Pillars of unusual design.
Signed 'Thomas Taylor Holburne'.
Probably the Thomas Taylor a Freeman of the Clockmakers' Company in 1646, Master in 1687 and died before 1692. His address, however, at one time was in the Strand.
Diams 53 and 48mm
Nelthropp Collection

35 Samuel Betts England c1660
Gold case, enamelled translucent green with central white daisy and border in relief of white flowers with pink markings. The cover similarly enamelled. Inside the case and cover are enamel paintings of scenery. Dial with white enamel chapter ring. Outside is an engraved gold rim and inside is green translucent enamel with a sunflower and border of flowers. Hand missing. The enamelling of the outside of the case is very badly chipped.
Three-wheel train. Cock with large oval foot and table covering the balance.
Signed 'Samuel Betts Londini'.
Betts was a Freeman of the Clockmakers' Company and died before 1675.
Diam 45mm

36 James Nellson England c1660
Egg-shaped undecorated silver case with bezel and glass.
Matt-gilt dial plate. Below is a silver chapter ring with an engraved scene and steel hand, probably replacement. Above is a silver day-of-month ring and a turning silver disc with pointer inside. There is an outer circle of months; then a circle with signs of the Zodiac; then a circle with a series of figures corresponding to the months, starting with February. A steel hand indicates on the three circles. On the left a sector aperture shows days of the week and engraved figures. On the right, an aperture shows the moon's phases, with apertures above and below showing the moon's age and (probably) times of high tide at some place.
Three-wheel train. Worm and wheel

set-up regulator. Pinned-on cock with narrow table.
Signed 'James Nellson Londini'.
Nellson was apprenticed in 1638.
Diams 53 and 43mm

37 John Wright England c1665
Movement only. Wheels missing. Cock with oval foot and circular table. Signed 'Johannes Wright in Covent Garden'. Wright was a Freeman of the Clockmakers' Company in 1661.
Diam 41mm
Presented by Mr Jackson, 1816

36a

36b

38 Jeremie Gregory c1670
Pair-case. The outer covered with leather and studded with gold. The inner plain circular rock-crystal with gilt mounts. Silver dial with an engraved scene in the centre. Single hand.
Oval cock. Worm-and-wheel set-up regulator. Tulip pillars. Signed 'Jeremie Gregory att the Royall Exchange'. Gregory was Master of the Clockmakers' Company in 1665.
Diams 50 and 40mm

39 Thomas Tompion c1671
Movement only. Long screwed-on cock. Worm-and-wheel set-up regulator with steel tracery part of which is missing. Signed 'Thomas Tompion, London' in flowing script.
This is the only known Tompion watch of the pre-balance-spring era. It is of high quality with no pinion of less than 6 leaves.
Diam 44mm
See also page 3

40 Daniel Carre [France] c1670
Silver pair-case. Outer case covered with oxidised iron studded with silver in floral pattern with a similar bezel. Inner case plain.
Gilt engraved dial plate. Small silver chapter ring below with segmental aperture showing day-of-the-week. Steel hand with long tail. Above, left, dial for day-of-month with engraved centre. On right, dial for age-of-moon with aperture for phases. Above, centre sector aperture for months.
Three-wheel train. Worm-and-wheel set-up regulator. Screwed-on cock with long oval foot and small oval table. Balance-spring added later.
Signed 'Daniel Carre'.
Diams 55 and 45mm
Nelthropp Collection

41 Jeremie Gregory England c1670
Silver case, pierced and engraved in openwork flowers and foliate design. Plain silver outer case, probably of later date. Split bezel, engraved. Round knob pendant.
Silver dial with engraved border. Raised hour circle. Central alarm disc with pointer. Steel hand with long tail. Three-wheel train. Cock with nearly circular table and very small foot. Worm-and-wheel set-up regulator with silver dial. Blued-steel winding stop. Centre wheel in recess in dial. Steel alarm crown wheel. Signed 'Jeremie Gregory at the Exchange'. Gregory was a Freeman of the Clockmakers' Company in 1652, Master in 1665, died 1685.
Diam 41mm
Nelthropp Collection

39

40a

41a

40b

40c

41b

42 Six unfinished watch movements
England c1670
Worm-and-wheel set-up. Cock with oval foot and circular table.
These six unfinished movements are complete and almost identical, although individual parts are not interchangeable. They represent a probably unique survival of evidence of quantity production in the seventeenth century. For later examples see 91 and 186.
Diam 41mm

43 Benjamin Wolverstone
England c1670
Silver pair-case. Outer case pierced, covered with leather and studded silver. Inner case has back and edge pierced and engraved in flower and foliage design. Dial gilt engraved border and silver hour ring. Alarm disc with pointer. Centre engraved with red enamel filling. Steel hand with long tail. Pendant loop with flat knob. Oval cock without rim, nearly covering the balance. Worm-and-wheel set-up regulator with openwork cover. Alarm train with steel crown and escape wheels.
Signed 'Ben Woluerstone Londini'. Wolverstone was apprenticed in 1649, a Freeman of the Clockmakers' Company in 1656 and died before 1690.
Diams 57 and 50mm

44 Cristinn Klein Schmit Austria c1674
Movement only. Dial gilt and champlevé with central alarm disc.
The case is of a much later date.
The movement was originally unsprung but a simple type of regulator and spring were added later. Worm-and-wheel set-up regulator. Alarm train. Cock with irregular-shaped foot and round table. Pierced alarm spring barrel and steel alarm wheels.
Signed 'Cristinn Klein Schmit a Wien'.
Diam 40mm
Presented by T.W. Jones, 1915

45 Ignatius Huggeford England c1675
Silver pair-case. Outer case covered with tortoiseshell studded with silver in a central pattern and round the edge and bezel. Inner case plain. Round pendant knob.
Dial has a gilt engraved edge border; then a turning silver day-of-month rim; then a matted silver ring with heart-shaped hour plaques; then a quarter band and a central pattern of four crowns. Steel arrow hand. Four-wheel train. Worm-and-wheel set-up regulator with silver dial and steel tracery. Blued-steel cock with large ruby centre, which is purely decorative, not an endstone.
Signed 'Ignatius Huggeford Londini'. Huggeford was admitted to the Clockmakers' Company in 1671.
This watch was successfully adduced by the Company to oppose Facio di Duillier's application in 1704 for prolongation of his patent for jewelling, on the ground that it proved prior use of a jewel as an endstone, although in fact it is decorative only.
Diams 53 and 45mm

45a

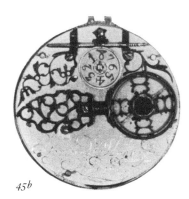

45b

45c

Verge escapement watches with balance-spring
For watches originally without balance-springs and subsequently converted see numbers 1, 4, 6, 25, 40, 44.

50a

50b

46

50c

46 Edward East England c1680
Single case covered in leather, not original.
White enamel dial, not original.
Four-wheel train. Balance-spring of two turns. Cock with irregular shaped foot and no mask. Signed 'Eduardus East London'.
Diam 50mm
See also page 3
Presented by F. Putley, 1816

47 Thomas Tompion England c1680
Pair-case, outer covered shagreen. Inner gilt. Stirrup pendant with flat top.
White enamel dial, probably replacement. Steel beetle and poker hands.
Four-wheel train. Irregular edge to cock foot. Signed 'Tho Tompion London' (not numbered and therefore prior to about 1680).
Tompion was born 1639, a Freeman of the Clockmakers' Company 1671, Master 1704, died 1713.
Diams 53 and 45mm
Presented by George Copeman, 1878

48 Thomas Tompion England c1680
Silver pair-case. Outer case covered tortoiseshell inlaid with silver in pattern of birds and flowers. Inner case plain. Stirrup pendant. White enamel dial. Both case and dial probably later. Steel beetle and poker hands.
Four-wheel train. Cock of unusual three-arm pattern and with no rim to foot. Balance-spring of 4 turns and therefore probably not the original spring. Signed 'Tho Tompion London' (not numbered and therefore prior to about 1680. May well be nearer 1676).
Diams 53 and 48mm
See also page 3
Presented by Charles E. Atkins
Illustrated on page 3

49 David Lainÿ [England] c1680
Movement only. No case.
White enamel dial of later date. Minute hand missing.
The cock is of English type. There is no hinge but instead a curved brass lug to fit into the case. Signed 'David Lainÿ'.
Diam 43mm
Presented by Edwin W. Streeter, 1885

50 William Bertram England c1680
Silver pair-case. The inner case has engraved 'J. Smith' and the outer a monogram 'J.S' both probably contemporary. Square hinge.
Silver champlevé six-hour dial with outer calendar ring.
Early type of balance-cock with no rim to foot. Signed 'Will Bertram. London'.
A maker of this name was Master of the Clockmakers' Company in 1732. This man is perhaps his father since the watch is of early balance-spring type.
Diams 50 and 44mm

51 Jonathan Growndes England c1680
Silver pair-case and an outer protective case.
Silver champlevé dial. Steel beetle and poker hands.
No rim to cock foot. Balance-spring of one turn. Barrow regulator. Signed 'Jonathan Growndes Fecit' on back plate and 'Grounds London' on dial.
Diams 53 and 45mm
Nelthropp Collection

52 Thomas Tompion England
c1680
Movement only. No dial.
Quarter-repeating mechanism of early
type. Movement signed 'Tho. Tompion
London'. Not numbered and therefore
prior to about 1680 which thus makes it
very early for a repeater.
Diam 41mm
Presented by Evan Roberts, 1904

53 Thomas Tompion England
c1682
Movement only. No dial.
Four-wheel train. Tulip pillars.
Signed 'T. Tompion London 0598'.
Tompion started numbering his work in
about 1680, and numbered pieces can be
fairly closely dated. However, he had a
series of numbers for what he considered
special pieces (for reasons not always
evident) and these do not seem to respond
to any date-pattern. This watch is of early
type and it therefore seems safe to date it
c1682.
Diam 38mm
Presented by B.L. Vulliamy, 1849

54 Thomas Tompion England
c1690
Movement only. Enamel dial of later type.
No rim to cock foot. Signed 'Tho Tompion
London 892' in script lettering.
This interesting watch has inconsistent
features which make it somewhat suspect
although it cannot be conclusively faulted

on any single one. The style of movement
suggests a date of c1680 but the number
belongs to the late 1690s. Tompion
usually repeated the number under the
cock foot but this is not so here. Unlike all
his contemporaries he almost invariably
fixed his balance-spring in a square hole
with a square pin; but this has the
conventional round hole and pin. The
signature is coarse for Tompion and the
decorative pillars are not characteristic of
him. The good quality dial and hands are
typical of c1730 but could be replacements.
Diam 40mm
Bequeathed by T. Vickery, 1946

55 Gordon D. Sinclare Ireland
c1690
Silver case, back and bezel engraved. Oval
loop pendant. Wandering hour dial.
Very large balance.
Signed 'Sinclare Dublin 146'.
Diam 55mm
See also page 4
Nelthropp Collection

56 Soret & Jay Probably Switzerland
c1685
Form watch in the shape of a dove, the
lower part of the body being hinged to
form the lid, which is engraved with a coat
of arms.
Silver dial engraved with a bird and
animals within scrolling foliage.
Signed 'Soret et Jay'.
The bird is 72mm long and 50mm high

55a

55b

55c

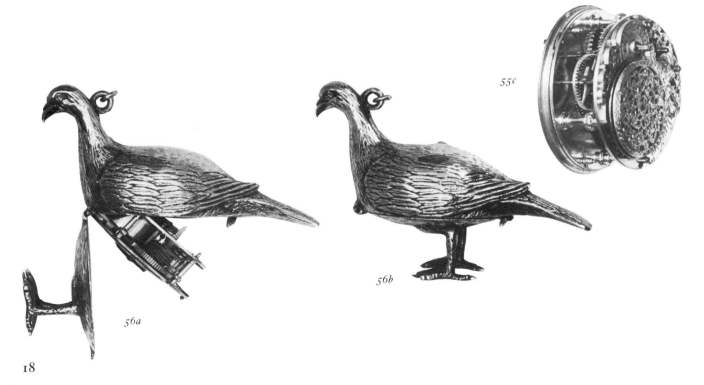

56a

56b

18

57 Anna Adamson England c1685
Pair-case. Inner gilt; outer covered with
leather and some pinwork (mostly
missing).
White enamel dial. Steel hands, tulip hour.
Movement with no rim to cock which is
pierced and engraved in a pattern of
lilies. Signed 'Anna Adamson fecit' (a very
early watch by a woman maker).
Diams 50mm and 43mm

58 Fromanteel [Holland] c1685
Movement only, no dial.
The fusee winding arbor comes through
the cock foot, which has two screws.
This feature and the design of the back
plate is peculiar to Ahasuerus Fromanteel
who lived and worked in The Hague and
Amsterdam. Signed 'Fromanteel'.
Diam 41mm
Presented by Edwin W. Streeter, 1875

59 Henry Jones England c1685
Single gilt case, the case, dial and hands
being of later date. No rim to cock.
Movement signed 'Henry Jones London'.
Jones was a Freeman of the Clockmakers'
Company in 1663, Master 1691, died 1695.
Diam 48mm
Presented by George Atkins, 1816

60 Nathaniel Barrow England
c1690
Silver pair-case. Stirrup pendant with flat
top. Gilt matt dial plate engraved with
cherubs. Below is a silver hour circle with
pierced centre. Steel hand with long tail.
Above is a silver ring showing day of
month with turning disc and pointer
inside. The disc has five circles. The outer
circle has the signs of the Zodiac; the
second the months; the third and fourth
the following series of figures:

4·36	4·49	5·21	6·0	6·39	7·1
21	23	23	23	23	22
7·24	7·11	6·39	6·0	5·21	4·49
21	19	18	20	20	21

The fifth circle shows the days in the
month. A sector aperture on the left shows
day of week and an aperture on the right
shows the moon's phase. There are two
small apertures, one showing the moon's
age and the other a double circle of 12 hours
on the moon plate (this probably gives the
time of high water at some port).
Three-wheel train. The cock, with very
large foot, and the rack and pinion
regulator appear to be later than the rest of
the watch which therefore may possibly
have been without a balance-spring
originally.

Signed 'Nathan Barrow London'.
Barrow was a Freeman of the Clockmakers'
Company in 1660, Master in 1689.
Diams 58 and 50mm

61 Nathaniel Barrow England
c1690
Pair-case. Outer gilt, undecorated. Inner
gilt with pierced and engraved edge.
Dial replacement.
Four-wheel train. Clock-watch with silver
count wheel. No rim to cock foot.
Signed 'Nath Barrow Londini' (see
preceding entry).
Diams 53 and 44mm
Presented by Joseph Penn, 1862

62 Robert Webster England c1690
Silver case. Edge and bezel pierced. Back
engraved with crest of lion rampant,
crowned. Pendant missing. Silver dial.
Signature in central space. Winding-holes
in dial. Two steel spade hands.
Clock-watch with parts of the striking
mechanism missing. Top plate with some
engraving and ratchet set-up.
Signed 'Robert Webster London'.
Webster was a Freeman of the
Clockmakers' Company in 1675, Master in
1704.
Diam 59mm

63 Benjamin Bell England c1690
Silver pair-case. Stirrup pendant.
Stamped S B.
Silver dial. Large subsidiary seconds dial
with raised decoration in sunk centre.
Steel tulip hands.
Steel balance-wheel with spring of three
turns. Cock with rim to balance and
rimless foot. Four-wheel train.
Signed 'Ben. Bell London'.
Bell was a Freeman of the Clockmakers'
Company 1657, Junior Warden in 1678,
Master 1682.
Diams 68 and 63mm
See also page 4
Nelthropp Collection
See also colour plate IV

64 James Hassenius England c1690
Movement only. No dial.
Movement incomplete.
Signed 'Ja. Hassenius. London Nº 1'.
Hassenius became a Freeman in 1682 as a
'brother alien'. According to G.H. Baillie
he returned to his native Russia in 1698.
Nelthropp Collection

65 Rodet England c1690
Silver case. No outer case, probably
re-cased. Sun and moon dial with a
seconds dial. Signed 'Rodet London'.
Diam 47mm

66 Henry Harper England c1690
Silver pair-case. Both cases pierced and
engraved in foliate design.
Silver dial. Centre sunk and repoussé
with figures and signature.
Steel beetle hands. Clock watch with silver
count-wheel sunk in top plate. Large
one-arm balance with short spring. Small
bridge-cock of Dutch type.
Signed 'Hen Harper London'.
Harper was a Freeman of the Clockmakers'
Company in 1664, Assistant 1682.
Diams 56 and 45mm
Presented by John W. Carter, 1898

65a

65b

68a

68b

68c

68d

67 Henry Harper England c1690
Movement only. No dial. Steel hands.
Regulation by arbor through dial and
index plate. Signed 'Harper London' (see
preceding entry).
Diam 40mm
Presented by G. & S.E. Atkins, 1850

68 Charles Gretton England c1690
Silver pair-case. Outer case pierced and
covered with leather studded with silver.
Inner case has edge pierced and back and
edge engraved. Stirrup pendant with flat
top. Silver dial with very long hour figures.
Alarm disc with pointer and short hand.
Small balance-wheel with spring of two
turns. Dial regulator.
Signed 'Charles Gretton London'.
Gretton was a Freeman of the
Clockmakers' Company 1672, Master
1700.
Diams 57 and 50mm

69 Daniel Le Count England c1690
Movement only.
Signed 'Daniel Le Count London 197'.
Le Count was a Freeman of the
Clockmakers' Company in 1676.
Diam 38mm
Presented by B.L. Vulliamy, 1818

70 Thomas Tompion England
End 17th century
Movement only. No rim to cock foot.
Signed 'Tho. Tompion 2268'.
Diam 41mm
Presented by Edwin W. Streeter, 1875

71 Edward Huntt England
End 17th century
Movement only. Incomplete.
Signed 'Edw. Huntt London'.
Huntt was a Freeman of the Clockmakers'
Company in 1684.
Diam 38mm
Presented by George Philcox, 1875

72 Brounker Watts England
Early 18th century
Gold case. Edge pierced and engraved.
Stirrup pendant. Outer case missing. Gold
dial. Sunk centre repoussé with name
plaques. Steel beetle hands. Quarter
repeating movement, repeating on bell or
pulse piece.
Engraved dust-cap with central pivoted
clip. Signed 'Brounker Watts London'.
Watts was a Freeman of the Clockmakers'
Company in 1693.
Diam 48mm
Presented by B.L. Vulliamy, 1816

73 Jasper Harmer England
Early 18th century
Silver pair-case. Stirrup pendant. Silver
dial. Sunk centre repoussé with name
plaques. Steel beetle hands.
The cock has a half-length figure of a
woman in an oval.
Signed 'Ias Harmer London'.
Diams 59 and 38mm
Presented by Miss Woodman, 1908

74 William Webster England
Early 18th century
Gold pair-case. Both outer and inner cases
pierced and engraved. Gold dial.
Sunk centre with name plaques. Steel
beetle hour hand. Later minute hand.
Repeating movement. Repeats on bell or
pulse piece. Pierced plaques on top plate.
Dust-cap engraved on top and rim.
Signed 'Willm. Webster Exchange Alley
London 1033'.
Webster was a journeyman with
Tompion. A Freeman of the Clockmakers'
Company 1710, Warden 1734, died the
same year.
Diams 53 and 48mm

75 Le Maire France or Holland
Early 18th century
Silver pair-case. White enamel dial with
arched minute bands. Gilt pierced hands.
Large bridge-cock. Winds through cock
and balance-wheel. Signed 'Le Maire'
Pierre Le Maire went from Paris to
Amsterdam in 1686. Jérémie Le Maire
went from Meaux to Amsterdam in 1687.
Before these dates Pierre was among the
first French makers of balance-spring
watches and pendulum clocks.
Diams 55 and 50mm
Nelthropp Collection

76 Cogniet France
Early 18th century
Cast gilt case in symmetrical design with
four busts. Bezel repoussé in foliate
pattern. White enamel dial with very large
hour figures and minute band inside. Dial
winding. Short hand (replacement).
Very large cock, solid and chiselled, with
slot and bob on balance. Egyptian pillars.
Signed 'Cogniet A Paris'.
This name is not recorded although there
were three Paris makers called Coignet.
Diam 58mm

77 Peter Debaufre England c1700
Plain silver case with small crystal in back
to show pirouette balance. Stirrup pendant
finely chased. Outer case missing. Silver
dial with raised figures. Steel beetle and
poker hands. Seconds dial with
decorative pierced hand. Stop piece
engaging with contrate wheel.
Verge escapement with pirouette, a wheel
of 60 on the verge-staff engaging with a
pinion of 6 on the balance-staff which thus
has an arc of about 2½ turns. The cock is a
rim with two thin arms to show pirouette
balance which has a spring with 4 turns.
Signed 'Peter Debaufre London' [Peter is
under the foot of the cock].
This watch was purchased by the
Company at Alexander Cumming's sale in
1815, and was probably reconstructed in
his workshop. There are three fine tulip
pillars, but the fourth is of Egyptian type.
Also as the foot of the cock covers 'Peter';
it is almost certainly not original. The top
plate has some curious marks but the hole
for the balance-staff is small and round,
not rectangular as is normal for a verge,
thus indicating that the pirouette is not a
conversion from a normal verge. The
potence is engraved which is unusual.
No jewelling.
Debaufre was *Maître* in Paris before 1675
and was a Freeman of the Clockmakers'
Company in 1689.
Diam 45mm

78 Simon Decharmes England
Early 18th century
Gold pair-case. Both cases pierced and
engraved. The outer case has a monogram
EB and a coronet. Gold dial. Sunk centre
repoussé with hour plaques. Steel tulip
hands.
Half-quarter repeater.
Signed 'S. Decharmes London'.
Decharmes was a Freeman of the
Clockmakers' Company in 1691.
The watch formerly belonged to the Duke
of Bridgewater.
Diams 53 and 48mm
Presented by B.L. Vulliamy, 1849
See also colour plate IV

79 Henry Overbury Holland
Early 18th century
Silver pair-case. The outer case
containing a Roman coin. Silver dial.
Steel beetle hands. Sunk seconds dial,
hand missing. Day-of-month aperture.
Cock with foot and slot to show bob on
balance. Engraved table.
Signed 'Henrij Overburij Rotterdam'.
Diams 61 and 53mm
Nelthropp Collection

80 William Andreas Enderlin
Switzerland   Early 18th century
Silver case, the back repoussé, edges
pierced and engraved, bezel engraved.
Gilt dial with enamel plaques for hours and
minutes. Steel hands. Bridge-cock with
enamel of Pero and Cimon. Repeating
movement. Signed 'An. Enderlin A Bale'.
Enderlin was born 1681 and died 1733. He
invented a frictional rest escapement.
Diam 56mm
Nelthropp Collection

81 Charles Goode England
Early 18th century
Movement only. White enamel dial. Steel
beetle hands. Large cock with ornamental
endstone.
Signed 'Charles Goode London'.
Goode was a Freeman of the Clockmakers'
Company and died 1735.
Diam 41mm
Nelthropp Collection

82 John Berry England
Movement early 18th century
Silver case with edge pierced and engraved,
and enamel dial, both of the
mid-eighteenth century.
Clock-watch striking on a bell.
Signed 'John Berry London'.
Diam 53mm

Berry was a Freeman of the Clockmakers'
Company in 1688, Master 1723.

83 Simon Decharmes England
Early 18th century
Movement only. White enamel dial and
steel beetle hands.
Signed 'S. De Charmes London'.
Decharmes was a Freeman of the
Clockmakers' Company in 1691.
Diam 38mm
Presented by B.L. Vulliamy, 1849

84 T. Tompion & E. Banger
England   Early 18th century
Movement only. Striking and repeating.
No dial. Signed 'T. Tompion,
E. Banger London 191'.
Edward Banger was nephew, apprentice
and assistant to Tompion. They were in
partnership from 1701 to 1708.
Banger was a Freeman of the Clockmakers'
Company in 1695.
Diam 41mm

85 Thomas Windmills England
Early 18th century
Movement only. Repeating. Rim cap
to movement. Signed 'Tho. Windmills
London'.
Diam 41mm
Presented by F.B. Adams & Sons, 1848

86 Langley Bradley England
Early 18th century
Movement only. Dust-cap. Stogden
repeating train.
Signed 'L. Bradley London NRO'.
Bradley was a Freeman of the
Clockmakers' Company 1695, Master
1726.
Diam 38mm
Presented by B.L. Vulliamy, 1820

87 David Lestourgeon England
Early 18th century
Movement only. White enamel dial. Steel
beetle hands.
Signed 'David Lestourgeon London 1386'.
Lestourgeon was a Freeman of the
Clockmakers' Company 1698.
Diam 43mm

88 Thomas Wightman England
Early 18th century
Silver pair-case. Outer case missing. Inner
case has the edge pierced in a pattern. Oval
loop pendant. White enamel dial. Steel
beetle hands. Clock-watch striking on
a bell.

Signed 'Tho Wightman London 405'.
Wightman was a Freeman of the
Clockmakers' Company 1696, died 1744.
Diam 50mm
Presented by Charles E. Atkins

89 Thomas Cartwright England
Early 18th century
Movement only.
The cock is a silver rim with a crystal table
and in the centre, a gold cap with a garnet.
Pierced plaque on top plate. Signed 'Thos.
Cartwright Principi Horologs. London'.
Cartwright was apprenticed in 1693.
Diam 38mm

90 Richard Bradshaw England
Early 18th century
Movement only. Enamel dial of Dutch
type with painted scene of a ship. Arched
minute hand. Gilt pierced hands. The
movement is probably English.
Signed 'Rd. Bradshaw London 591'.
Bradshaw was a Freeman of the
Clockmakers' Company 1725.
Diam 38mm
Nelthropp Collection

91 Anonymous England
Early 18th century
Watch movement in the grey. Semi-broad-
foot cock, not yet pierced. Fusee uncut.
Centre seconds.
Diam 50mm
Presented by F.B. Adams & Sons, 1848

92 Cornelis Uyterweer Holland
Early 18th century
Movement only. White enamel dial.
Gilt pierced hands.
Silver cock with slot and glass showing a
bob on the balance, and with a figure
holding a sword and the motto
'Quid hac absente juvat'. Signed
'C. Uyterweer Rotterdam No. 527'.
Diam 38mm

93 Francis Colman England
Early 18th century
Movement only. Cock with slot showing
bob on balance. Engraved pattern on table
and engraving on top plate below slot.
Signed 'Fr. Colman Ipswich'.
Diam 40mm

94 Peter Amyot England
Early 18th century
Movement only. Skeleton top plate.
Signed 'Peter Amyot Norwich 5825'.
Diam 43mm

95 Thomas Tompion England
c1700
Movement only. Later enamel dial.
Steel beetle hands.
Large cock with rim to foot.
Signed 'Thos. Tompion London 2920'.
Diam 38mm
Presented by Sir John Thorold Bt, 1818

96 Henry Massy England c1700
Movement only. Enamel dial of later date.
Tulip pillars. Winds through dial but as
there is also a square on the back plate this
may be a conversion. Signed
'Hen. Massy London 809' in early type of
script.
Diam 40mm
Bequeathed by T. Vickery, 1946

97 Thomas Tompion England
c1700
Silver pair-case. Square hinge.
Punchmark ws. White enamel dial and
hands replacements.
Broad cock foot. Worm set-up.
Signed 'T. Tompion London 896'.
Diam 55mm
Collinson Collection

98 Matthew Gleave England c1700
Movement only. No dial. Train has an
extra wheel and pinion despite which the
going time is only about 35 hours.
Signed 'Matʷ Gleave'.
Gleave worked in Derby. Died 1705.
Diam 45mm
Presented by F. Putley, 1816

99 Christopher Gould England
c1700
Gilt-metal pair-case. The silver pendant
bow is later. Punchmark RC. Silver dial not
original. Repoussé signed
'Hathaway London'.
Movement with tulip pillars. No rim to
cock foot. Mask with cherub's head.
Signed 'C. Gould London'.
Gould was a Freeman of the Clockmakers'
Company in 1682, died 1718.
Diams 55 and 45mm
Collinson Collection

100 Charles Gretton England c1700
Silver pair-case. Bezel missing. Silver dial.
No minute figures. One steel tulip hand.
No rim to cock foot. Pierced plaque on top
plate. Signed 'Charles Gretton London'.
Gretton was apprenticed in 1662.
Admitted to the Clockmakers' Company
1672, Master 1700.

Diams 53 and 45mm
Nelthropp Collection

101 Martin Elwood England c1700
Silver pair-case. Outer case covered in
tortoiseshell and inlaid silver in pattern of
birds and foliage. Silver dial. Centre
chiselled in foliate pattern. Steel tulip
hands.
No rim to cock foot.
Signed 'Martin Elwood London'.
Elwood was a Freeman of the
Clockmakers' Company in 1687.
Diams 50 and 44mm
Presented by George Atkins, 1825

102 Richard Street England c1700
Single silver case. An equation of time
scale is engraved on the back, having an
outer circle of months and an inner circle
of minutes. Open cover to case and an
inner bezel with glass. Round knob
pendant. Silver dial with no signature.

101

Normal hour circle but minute ring numbered 1–15, the minute hand going round in fifteen minutes. Each minute has six divisions of 10 seconds each. Movement of very high quality with reversed fusee. The regulator is by worm and rack. Signed 'Richard Street London 408' (the case also is stamped 408). Street was admitted to the Clockmakers' Company in 1687 and was Junior Warden in 1715, in which year he probably died. Street worked for Sir Isaac Newton. There is a long-case clock by him at the Greenwich Observatory with a similar dial, the minute hand going round in 15 minutes.
Diam 67mm
See also page 4
Nelthropp Collection

103 Dirk Koster Holland c1700
Silver pair-case. Outer case cast in a figure scene. Silver dial. Sun and moon hour indicator. Gilt pierced minute hand (replacement). Below, a day of month aperture surrounded by high relief decoration.
Dutch bridge-cock of silver, pierced. Silver pierced plaque on top plate. Conical fluted pillars.
Signed 'Dirk Koster Amsterdam'.
Diams 56 and 48mm
Presented by John N. Dymond, 1881.

104 Francis Raynsford England c1700
Square silver case covered with leather, silver studded. Square dial. No minute figures. Sunk seconds dial. Two steel beetle hands. Stop-lever on arbor through dial engaging the escape-wheel.
Signed 'Fr Raynsford London'.
Raynsford was a Freeman of the Clockmakers' Company 1689.
44mm square and 18mm deep

105 Paul Roumieu Scotland c1700
Movement only. Gilt dial with eccentric hour dial and slot below to show a bob on the balance. Steel beetle hands.
Signed 'Paul Roumieu Edinburgh 259'.

Diam 41mm
Nelthropp Collection

106 Joseph Gray England c1700
Movement only. No dial. Barrow-type regulator. For some unknown reason the foot of the cock has been filed flat and its edges shaped. Signed 'Joseph Gray, Shaston' (contraction of Shaftesbury).
Diam 40mm
Presented by C.R. Harle, 1875

107 Nicholas Massy England c1700
Movement only. No dial. Balance spring missing. Cock of French bridge type with steel regulator arm pivoted on the cock, carrying block for the spring in a slot at the edge of the cock. Very small escape-wheel. Engraving on top plate.
Signed 'Nicholas Massy London'.
Massy was a Freeman of the Clockmakers' Company in 1693.
Diam 38mm
Presented by George Atkins, 1818

102a

102b

104a

104b

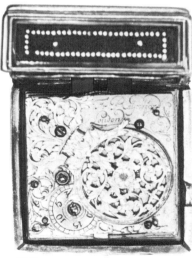

104c

108 M. Martinot France c1700
Gilt-metal case covered in polished black
fish-skin. Repoussé gold dial. Large
enamel hour plaques and inner enamel
band. In the centre a repoussé bust of
Louis XIV. Short steel hand. Winding at
centre. Knob pendant.
Very large cock nearly full size of the plate,
solid except for a half-circular slot
showing a bob on the balance and
regulator figures for the rack and pinion
regulator below. Engraved table.
Egyptian pillars.
Signed 'M. Martinot A Avignon'.
Diam 57mm
See also page 5
Presented by The Hon Anne Seymour
Damer

109 Henry Massy England c1700
Silver pair-case. Outer case with square
hinge. Stirrup pendant.
Silver dial. Steel hands.
Pierced plaques on top plate. Broad-footed
cock with rim.
Signed 'Henry Massy London 2071'.
Massy was a Freeman of the Clockmakers'
Company in 1692.
Diams 53 and 44mm
Nelthropp Collection

110 J. Jaque André Bosset France
c1700
Silver case. White enamel dial with very
large hour figures. Single steel hand.
Dial winding.
Large cock with enamel figure of a girl and
a canary. A small silver heart, connected to,
and bent over from the balance, moves
over the top of her head. Signed
'I. Iaque André Bosset A la Neuveville'.
Diam 57mm
Nelthropp Collection

111 Hélie Boursault France c1700
Silver case, very deep and plain. Round
pendant knob and ring. Silver domed dial
with raised hour figures on matt ground in
cartouches with raised borders. Small
steel hand. Dial winding.
Very large bridge-cock with very small
eyes. Solid with slot showing a bob on the
balance.
Signed 'Helie Bovrsavlt A Chatellerault'.
Diam 58mm
Nelthropp Collection

112 David Lestourgeon England
c1700
Silver pair-case. Silver dial with eccentric
hour ring and slot below showing a bob on

108a

108b

the balance. Steel beetle hands. There is a
regulator dial on each side of the bob
aperture. Engraved gilt plate over top
plate with a central repoussé bust of
William III. Signed 'Lestourgeon London'
on movement and 'Lesturgeon' on dial.
Lestourgeon was a Freeman of the
Clockmakers' Company 1698.
Diams 53 and 45mm
Nelthropp Collection

113 Fromanteel England c1700
Gilt-metal single case covered tortoise-
shell. Stirrup pendant. Enamel dial,
possibly not original.
Repeating movement.
Signed 'Fromanteel London 1720'.
Diam 55mm
Presented by G.S. Sanders

114 Daniel Quare England c1700
Single gilt-metal case covered on back and
bezel with horn to imitate agate. Edges
gold studded. Stirrup pendant. White
enamel dial possibly later. Gold beetle
hands, replacements. Dial winding.
Sector and keyhole for regulator.
Very large balance. Diamond endstone in
silver cap. Silver dust-cap.
Signed 'Quare London 3208'.
Quare was born 1649. A Freeman of the
Clockmakers' Company 1671, Master
1708, died 1724.
Diam 53mm

115 Daniel Quare England c1700
Movement only. White enamel dial and
hands later. Dial winding.
Very large balance and cock with unusual
decoration. Egyptian pillars with foliage.
Signed 'Daniel Quare London 3543'.
Diam 40mm
Presented by Miss Woodman, 1908

116 Christopher Egleton England
c1700
Silver pair-case. Outer case covered
tortoiseshell silver studded. Knob
pendant. Square hinge. Stamped '375'.
Silver dial. Sunk repoussé centre with
name plaque, name erased. Tulip hands.
Cock engraved with birds, squirrels and
foliage. Signed 'Chr. Egleton London 375'.
Egleton was a Freeman of the
Clockmakers' Company 1695.
Diams 53 and 48mm
See also page 5
Presented by B.L. Vulliamy, 1816
See also colour plate III

117 George Etherington England
Early 18th century
Later silver-gilt case, HM 1780–1.
Later silver dial with engine-turned
centre. Later gold hands.
Ruby endstone in silver cap. Dumb
repeater. Signed 'George Etherington
London 1086'.
Etherington was a Freeman of the
Clockmakers' Company in 1684, Master
1709.
Diam 50mm
Presented by John W. Carter, 1902

116a

116b

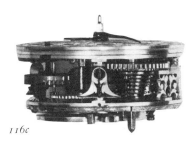

116c

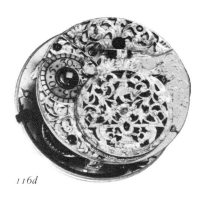

116d

118 Thomas Windmills England
c1700
Silver engraved pair-case of somewhat
Dutch style. Dial and hands of later date.
Silver cock and dust-cap.
Signed 'Thos Windmills London 6079'.
G.H. Baillie considered this watch was a
forgery but there seems no strong reason to
question the authenticity of the movement,
which is a repeater. However, the
engraving of the outer case is Continental
in style.
Diams 58 and 48mm

119 J. Banks England HM1701
Silver pair-case with London hallmark for
1701. This is the earliest hallmark in the
collection. Punchmark RB. Silver
repoussé dial with centre cartouche
signed 'Banks, Nottingham'. Broad-foot
cock signed 'J. Banks Nottingh^m.'.
Diams 56 and 48mm
Presented by F.W. May, 1963

120 John Bushman England c1700
Silver pair-case. Outer case repoussé in a
simple pattern. Stirrup pendant. Silver
differential dial. Between the narrow
minute band and the small rotating hour
disc is a band with repoussé trophy of
arms and name plaques below. Hand is
replacement. Engraved on back of case is
'James Bann'.
Signed 'John Bushman London'.
Diams 50 and 45mm
Nelthropp Collection

120a

120b

121a

121b

121c

121 Charles Gretton England
HM1702–3
Gold pair-case. Outer case chased in a
pattern to look like engine-turning. Square
hinge. Knob pendant. Gold dial. Sunk
repoussé centre with name plaque. Steel
hands. The top verge pivot-hole was a ruby
in a silver cap, now missing, and probably
not original (Facio did not take out his
Patent until 1704).
Signed 'Charles Gretton London'.
Diams 56 and 48mm
See also page 5

122 Loundes England c1705
Silver pair-case. Square hinge. Later
pendant. Punchmark MN. Silver repoussé
dial signed 'Loundes London'. Hands
replacements.
Broad-foot cock with wings.
Signed 'Loundes in Pallmall'.
Three members of this family practised in
Pall Mall at this time, each usually signing
his full name.
Diams 58 and 49mm
Collinson Collection

123 Joseph Jackman England c1705
Movement only. No dial. Steel beetle
hands.
Signed 'Jos. Jackman. London Bridg.'.
Diam 43mm
Presented by F. Barraud, 1818

124 Richard Vick c1705
Pair-case. Inner gold, pierced and
engraved. Outer gilt, replacement. Later
enamel dial and hour hand.
Repeats on a bell. Silver cock with
diamond endstone. Engraved silver
dust-cap.
Signed 'Richd Vick London 196'.
Diams 57 and 50mm

125 Daniel Quare England c1708
Silver pair-case, both pierced and
engraved. White enamel dial. Steel beetle
hands.
Movement with diamond endstone.
Repeater. Signed 'Daniel Quare London
722'.
Quare had a separate numbering series for
repeaters and this is a fairly high number
perhaps suggesting a later date than 1708
which was attributed to it (no doubt with
a good reason) by G.H. Baillie.
Diams 45 and 43mm
Nelthropp Collection

126 Daniel Quare England c1710
Gold pair-case. The hallmark, which is
difficult to decipher, looks like an N which
is the mark for 1728. If so, the case is
certainly later than the movement whose
number suggests a date c1710. Quare's
watches with dial winding and regulating,
as here, usually had a single case, which
also suggests that this case may be a
replacement, although the casemaker's
stamp IR is the same as is found on Quare's
single cases, e.g. number 132.
Gold dial with central name plaque with
dial winding at III and regulating dial and
square at XII. Steel hands with heavy
cranked minute hand as used by Quare to
avoid the winding square.
Cock with solid engraved foot, typical of
Quare's later work, with diamond
endstone. Signed 'Daniel Quare London
3720'.
The watch has a gold chain and cranked
key attached.
Diams 53 and 45mm
See also page 5
Presented by Sir David Salomons Bt, 1924

126a

126b

127 **William Gib** Holland c1710
Movement only. White enamel dial with
arcaded minute band. Gold fleurs-de-lys
between the hour figures. Steel beetle
hands. Silver Dutch bridge-cock with slot
and glass showing bob on balance. On the
table is chiselled a figure holding two
flaming hearts and motto '*D'une même
flame*'. Signed 'Willm Gib Rotterdam'.
Diam 38mm
Nelthropp Collection

128 **R. Threlkeld** England c1710
Movement only. Gold dial. Name plaques
in centre. Steel beetle hands.
Signed 'R. Threlkeld in the Strand'.
Diam 43mm
Nelthropp Collection

129 **Tompion & Graham** England
c1711
Case, dial and hands are not original.
Signed 'Tho. Tompion Geo. Graham
London 4504'.
Diam 52mm
Collinson Collection

130 **Tompion & Graham** England
c1711
Movement only. White enamel dial. Steel
beetle hands. Signed 'Tho. Tompion, Geo.
Graham London 4369'.
Tompion and Graham were in partnership
from 1711–13. This is about the earliest
recorded number of the partnership.
Diam 43mm

131 **Daniel Quare** England c1712
Painted enamel case signed '*Les Frères
Huaud*'. Inside of case is yellow enamel.
Silver repoussé dial with Huaud enamel
centre. Dial winding. Steel hands, tulip
hour.
Broad-foot winged cock.
Signed 'Quare, London' (no number).
The combination of a Quare watch (or any
English movement) in a Huaud enamelled
case is very unusual.
Diam 45mm
See also page 5
See also colour plate III

132 **Quare & Horseman** England
c1720
Single silver case covered in leather.
Stirrup pendant. Stamped IR.
Silver dial. Sunk centre with name
plaques. Dial winding. Steel hands with
cranked minute hand to avoid winding
square. Signed 'Quare & Horseman
London 5408'.

Quare and Horseman were in partnership
from 1718–24 when Quare died but
Horseman continued to use both names up
to the date of his bankruptcy in 1733.
Diam 44mm

133 **Windmills** England c1720
Gold pair-case, the outer repoussé.
Stamped IL.8905. Stirrup pendant. Gold
dial. Name plaques in sunk centre. Steel
beetle hands.
Signed 'Windmills London 8905'.
This watch is in almost new condition. It
was probably made during the partnership
of Joseph and his son Thomas which
started about 1700.
Joseph was a Freeman of the Clockmakers'
Company in 1671 and was Master in 1702.
Thomas was a Freeman in 1695 and was
Master in 1718.
Diams 50 and 43mm
See also page 6
Nelthropp Collection

134 **J. Stevenson** England c1720
Movement only. No dial. Twisted
baluster pillars. Signed 'J. Stevenson' (in
script, then) 'STAFFORD' (in capitals).
Diam 40mm
Bequeathed by T. Vickery, 1946

135 **Thomas Windmills** England
c1720
Silver pair-case, inner pierced, outer
repoussé, stamped SI.IL.7903.
Silver repoussé dial. Hands later.
Quarter repeater. Ruby endstone to
balance. Signed 'Tho. Windmills.
London 7903'.
Diams 49 and 43mm
Collinson Collection

136 **Daniel Delander** England c1720
Movement only. No dial. Repeater.
Signed 'Danl. Delander. London'.
Diam 42mm
Bequeathed by T. Vickery, 1946

137 **Quare & Horseman** England
c1720
Movement only. Unusual dial plate.
Diamond endstone. Dust-cap.
Signed 'Quare & Horseman London 1117'.
Diam 37mm
Presented by F.B. Adams & Sons, 1850

138 **George Graham** England c1723
Movement only. White enamel dial. Gold
beetle hands.

133a

133b

133c

Diamond endstone in blued cap.
Signed 'Geo. Graham London 5074'.
Diam 38mm
Presented by Sir John Thorold Bt, 1818

139 William Gib Holland c1725
Movement only. White enamel dial with
arcaded minute ring.
Cock with foot and slot to show bob on
balance. Very wide Egyptian pillars.
Signed 'William Gib Rotterdam 1653'.
Diam 45mm
Presented by Edwin W. Streeter, 1875

140 Pieter Gib Holland c1725
Movement only. White enamel dial with
arcaded minute ring.
Cock with slot to show bob on balance,
with chiselled scene of a child reading and
motto '*L'Eloquence*'. Pierced plaques on
top plate.
Signed 'P. Gib Rotterdam No. 172'.
Diam 38mm
Nelthropp Collection

141 Daniel Clerk Holland c1725
Movement only. White enamel dial. Gilt
pierced hands.
Cock with slot and glass to show bob on
pendulum.
Signed 'Daniel Clerk Amsterdam'.
Diam 37mm
Nelthropp Collection

142 Debaufre [Holland] c1730
Silver repoussé pair-case signed 'Cochin'.
Baillie considered this signature and that
on the movement are forgeries. Cochin
made repoussé cases between 1732 and
1770 in Geneva and Paris. There is
another authentic signature by him in the
collection, see numbers 165, 224.
Movement signed 'Debaufre London' but
all in the Dutch style.
Diams 54 and 47mm

143 William Gough England c1730
Originally pair-case, outer missing. Silver
inner. Stirrup pendant. Silver dial. Sunk
matt centre with name plaques. Steel
beetle hands.
A sliding rod in the pendant engages a slide
moved by hour and quarter snails enabling
the time to be told by touch.
Signed 'Will. Gough London 475'.
Diam 43mm
Presented by B.L. Vulliamy, 1816

144 Benjamin Gray England
HM 1730-1
Gold pair-case. Outer repoussé with head
of Apollo. The bezel of inner case has been
removed so that inner will fit (very
tightly) into the fine outer which has been
fitted with a glass. Stirrup pendant. White
enamel dial. Steel beetle hour hand.
Minute hand missing. Dial winding.
Diamond endstone in silver cap. Silver
rim cap. Dumb repeater with one hammer.
Signed 'Benj. Gray London r.s.c.'.
Gray was watchmaker to George II, born
1676, died 1764.
Diams 44 and 38mm
Presented by B.L. Vulliamy, 1830

145 D. Delander England c1730
Movement only, no dial, but hands
survive. Unusual and curious pillars.
Flat-cut ruby endstone secured by three
screws.
Signed 'D. Delander. London 668'.
Diam 42mm
Bequeathed by T. Vickery, 1946

146 Thomas Schardees [Holland]
c1730
Silver pair-case. No marks, but outer has a
foreign coronet and PK roughly engraved
on it.
White enamel dial with arcaded minute
band. Continental hands. Signed 'Tho
Schardees London 1134', but the style of
the watch and the rather unlikely name
suggest foreign manufacture.
Diams 58 and 51mm
Nelthropp Collection

147 Edward Faulkner England
c1730
Gold pair-case, both pierced and chased.
Outer stamped RH.576. White enamel dial
of later date.
Clock watch with rack-striking. Engraved
barrel. Pierced cock foot with mask.
Signed 'Edwd Faulkner London 576'.
Faulkner was apprenticed 1692, a
Freeman of the Clockmakers' Company
1702, Master in 1734.
Diams 50 and 44mm

148 Anonymous [Holland] c1730
Movement only. White enamel dial with
arcaded minute band and coloured scenic
centre. Replacement.
Broad-foot cock with slot for bob on
balance. The signature on the movement
has been filed off.
Diam 44mm
Nelthropp Collection

149 David Hubert England c1730
Movement only, no dial. Very small
quarter-repeating movement.
Signed 'David Hubert London 1753' on
back plate and dust-cap.
Diam 26mm

150 N. Cartwright England c1730
Movement only. White enamel dial. Gilt
pierced hands. Silver plate pillars.
Signed 'N. Cartwright Lombard Street
London 2100'.
Diam 38mm
Presented by Samuel E. Atkins, 1875

151 Christopher Pinchbeck England
c1730
Movement only. White enamel dial.
Signed 'Cr. Pinchbeck London. 56'.
Diam 35mm
Presented by B.L. Vulliamy, 1816

152 Jean Baron Holland c1735
Movement only. White enamel dial with
arcaded minute ring. Gold hands. Large
balance. Pierced plaque on top plate.
Egyptian pillars with foliate chiselling.
Signed 'Jean Baron Utrecht'.
Diam 44mm
Presented by Edwin W. Streeter, 1875

153 William Kipling England c1735
Movement only. Silver dial. Day of month
aperture. Name plate. Steel beetle hands.
Wheel-type cock with a glass. Unusual
pillars. Silver rim cap with masks and
tracery.
Signed 'Will. Kipling London. 1833'.
Diam 40mm
Presented by A.A.E. Lecluse, 1901

154 Solomon Julliot England c1738
Movement only. No dial.
Signed 'Sol. Julliot, London 413'.
The date 1738 is on the mainspring.
Diam 26mm
Presented by F.B. Adams, c1850

155 Paillion France c1740
Gilt case. Back and bezel with an
enamelled scene. White enamel dial. Gilt
beetle hands. Dial winding. Coqueret with
a stone. Signed 'Paillion Paris 902'.
Diam 46mm
Nelthropp Collection

156 Julien Le Roy [France] c1740
Porcelain case with scene on back in red.
Three scenes in red on porcelain bezel.

Gold frames. Stirrup pendant. White enamel dial. Steel beetle hands. Dial winding.
French bridge-cock with ruby endstone. Large silver regulator dial. Potence adjustment with very large screw head. Signed 'Le Roij A Paris'. The 'ij' suggests a Dutch forgery but the workmanship is fully up to Le Roy's standard.
Diam 45mm
Nelthropp Collection
See also colour plate IV

157 Paul du Pin England
HM 1739–40
Triple case, middle and inner gold. Outer covered leather. Middle repoussé with a classical subject in high relief, signed 'Moser'. Inner pierced with engraved edge. Stirrup pendant. White enamel dial. Gold beetle hands.
Quarter repeater on bell or touch-piece in bezel of middle case. Dust-cap.
Signed 'Paul du Pin London 1530'.
Diams 53, 45 and 38mm

158 James Snelling England
HM 1744–5
Gold pair-case. The outer, engine-turned, is a replacement and is hallmarked 1807–8. Inner with edge pierced and engraved. Stirrup pendant.
White enamel dial with Arabic figures, probably dating from the time of fitting the outer case in 1807; also the gold arrow hands. Silver cock. Silver tracery work over the whole top plate. Dust-cap.
Signed 'J. Snelling London 2107'.
Snelling was a Freeman of the Clockmakers' Company 1712, became Master 1736, died 1751.
Diams 48 and 43mm

159 George Lindsay England c1740
Pair-case. Outer has lost its (probably leather) covering, punchmark PM.
White enamel dial. Signed 'G. Lindsay. Sert to his Majesty. 488'.
Diam 51mm
Collinson Collection

160 Alexander Le Bon France c1740
Movement only. White enamel dial. No hands.
Lens-shaped cock with geometrical pattern. Screw-adjusted potence.
Signed 'Le Bon A Paris'.
Diam 38mm
Presented by Samuel E. Atkins, 1885

161 John Hocker England c1740
Movement only. White enamel dial. Blued beetle hands. Tulip pillars.
Signed 'John Hocker, Reading'.
Diam 38mm
Presented by Edwin W. Streeter, 1875

162 Dirk Van Winden Holland c1740
Movement only. Silver embossed dial. Unusually for a Dutch watch the minute ring is not arcaded. Calendar aperture. Gilt pierced hands.
Glazed slot in cock to show bob on balance. Signed 'Dirk Van Winden, Schiedam'.
Diam 48mm

163 Henry Overbury Holland c1740
Movement only. White enamel dial with arcaded minute ring. Gold spade hands (hour broken). Quarter repeater. English-type cock.
Signed 'Henry Overbury. Overschie'.
Diam 45mm
Presented by Evan Roberts, 1904

164 Michel Preudhomme
[Holland or Switzerland] c1740
Movement only. White enamel dial with arcaded minute ring. Pierced gilt hands. Dutch-type cock. Pierced plaque on top plate. Signed 'Michel Prevdhomme'.
The style of the watch is Dutch but a Paul Preudhomme worked in Geneva.
Diam 42mm
Nelthropp Collection

165 Demelais [Holland] c1740
Silver repoussé case, signed 'D. Cochin'. Arcaded minute ring. Date aperture. Continental bridge-cock with circular table. Ornate pillars. Worm and pinion set-up. Signed 'Demelais London'.
Diam 57mm
Collinson Collection

166 Markwick Markham England c1740
Movement only. Silver cock.
Signed 'Markwick Markham London 6732'.
Diam 41mm

167 Thomas Mudge England c1740
Movement only. White enamel dial. Steel beetle hands.
Cock with solid, engraved foot. Diamond endstone.

Signed 'Tho. Mudge London 244'. Mudge was born 1715, admitted to the Clockmakers' Company 1738, died 1794. An early example of his work which generally has a cylinder escapement.
Diam 35mm
Nelthropp Collection

168 William Scafe England
HM 1742–3
Pair-case. Outer gilt with monogram JMS in chased border of wreaths. Inner gold. White enamel dial. Gold arrow hands. Ruby endstone. Pierced plaques on top plate. Name on rim of cock.
Signed 'Wm. Scafe London. 449'.
Scafe was a Freeman of the Clockmakers' Company 1721, Master 1749.
Diams 50 and 43mm

169 John Nerry England c1745
Movement only. No dial. Incomplete. Unusual pillars.
Signed 'Jn. Nerry, London. 233'.
Diam 45mm
Presented by Edwin W. Streeter, 1875

170 Julien Le Roy France c1740
Movement only. No dial. Gold pierced hands. Lens-shaped bridge-cock with coqueret. Screw-adjusted potence. Oil-sinks throughout. Signed 'Julien Le Roy A Paris 2721'.
Julien Le Roy, 1686–1759, invented oil-sinks.
Diam 38mm
Presented by B.L. Vulliamy, 1849

171 William Paty England c1740
Movement only. White enamel dial. Steel beetle hands.
The end of the table of the cock has a lug which is screwed to the plate.
Signed 'Wm Paty London 204'.
Diam 38mm
Presented by B.L. Vulliamy, 1816

172 Isaac Duhamel Mid 18th century
Triple case. Outer consists of two bezels, each with a glass, covered tortoiseshell, gold studded. Middle case gold repoussé in high relief. Inner gold with edge pierced and engraved. White enamel dial with no minute figures. Steel spade hands, the dial and hands replacements.
Quarter repeater on bell. Diamond endstone. Silver dust-cap. Signed 'Isaac Duhamel London 167'.
Diams 56, 48 and 40mm

173 Pierre Michaud France
Mid 18th century
Gold case, engraved. Oval loop pendant.
White enamel dial. Gold pierced hands.
Dial winding. Ruby endstone.
Signed 'Pr. Michaud Paris'.
Diam 31mm
Nelthropp Collection

174 Joseph White England
Mid 18th century
Movement only. White enamel dial.
Diamond endstone. Silver plate on top
plate with signature.
Signed 'Jos. White London 756'.
White was a Freeman of the Clockmakers'
Company 1714, died 1766.
Diam 38mm
Nelthropp Collection

175 Samuel Ruel Holland
Mid 18th century
Movement only. White enamel dial
perhaps not original. Gilt pierced hands.
Cock with slot showing bob on balance
and chiselled scene of a seated man with
compasses and globe and a motto
'*L'Astronomie*'. Signed 'S. Ruel
Rotterdam No. 288'.
Diam 41mm
Nelthropp Collection

176 H. van Overklift & W. Loon
Holland Mid 18th century
Movement only. White enamel dial with
signature. Minutes at quarters.
Silver cock with slot showing bob on
balance. Chiselled design of a female figure
and a building with motto '*De
Standvastigheit*'. Hinged dust-cap with
glass over cock. Signed 'Hy. van Overklift
Wm. Loon A Dordrecht'.
Diam 43mm
Nelthropp Collection

177 Cornu France Mid 18th century
Movement only. White enamel dial.
Pierced gold hand. Dial winding.
Silver lens-shaped cock with wheel design.
Blued coqueret with ornamental endstone.
Signed 'Cornu a Montpellier'.
Diam 38mm
Presented by Samuel E. Atkins, 1873

178 Thomas Parker Ireland
Mid 18th century
Movement only. White enamel dial. Steel
beetle hands.
Regulator dial let into foot of cock.
Signed 'Thos. Parker Dublin 786'.

Diam 38mm
Nelthropp Collection

179 Faguillon France
Mid 18th century
Movement only. No dial. Large cock of
unusual design.
Signed 'Faguillon a Hesdin'.
Diam 38mm
Presented by F.B. Adams & Sons, 1849

180 Anonymous
France or Switzerland Mid 18th century
Movement only. White enamel dial. Dial
winding. Dumb repeater.
Diam 27mm
Presented by Samuel E. Atkins, 1875

181 [George Graham]
Mid 18th century
Watch, forgery of George Graham.
Signed 'Geo. Graham London 723'.
Diam 54mm

182 Jean Antoine Lepine France
Mid 18th century
Glass case in gilt bezels with border of
diamonds. White enamel dial. Gilt sun
hour hand. Dial winding.
Very small cock with coqueret. Balance is
over a bright steel ring. The top plate is
covered with silver tracery studded with
diamonds. Signed 'Lepine A Paris'.
Lepine, 1720–1814, was watchmaker to
Louis XV.
Diam 38mm

183 James Grantham England
c1750
Porcelain case and bezel, white, with
painted group of flowers and, inside the
case, a painted fly. Gold frames. Stirrup
pendant. White enamel dial. Steel beetle
hands. Dial winding.
Signed 'J. Grantham London 2980'.
Diam 42mm
Nelthropp Collection
See also colour plate III

184 Andrew Dickie Scotland c1750
Movement only. Dial and hands
replacements.
Broad-footed cock. Square pillars.
Signed 'And Dickie, Sterling'.
Diam 38mm
Nelthropp Collection

185 [George Graham] England
c1750
Silver pair-case stamped in three places

DAG. White enamel dial probably not
original as it seems to have been reduced in
size to fit this watch. Continental hands.
Silver cock with coqueret. Fine silver
pillars. Signed 'Geo. Graham, London',
but certainly a Continental forgery. The
lettering is not of a type used by Graham
who invariably numbered his work and
this has no number.
Diams 51 and 43mm
Bequeathed by M.L. Bateman, 1966

186 Anonymous England c1750
Two watch movements in the grey. One,
very small, diam 15mm, is without fusee
or balance. The other, 38mm, has semi-
broad-foot cock. Both have circular pillars.

187 John Jefferys England
HM 1752–3
Silver pair-case. White enamel dial
(blackened as the result of fire). Centre
seconds.
John Harrison's special type of verge
escapement with diamond pallets. Has the
first maintaining power to be incorporated
in any watch. Compensation curb, the
first temperature compensation in any
watch. Signed 'John Jefferys London' on
back plate and 'John Jefferys. London.
AD.1753' on dust-cap. For further
particulars and history of this highly
important watch see introduction to this
section.
Diams 62 and 54mm
Presented by Hull Trinity House

188 Joseph Wood England
HM 1754–5
Gold pair-case. White enamel dial. Centre
seconds hand between hour and minute
beetle hands.
Maker's initials pierced on cock table.
Signed 'Jos. Wood Scarborough 581'.
Diams 48 and 41mm
Presented by Executors of
Colonel J.R. Sandwith, 1926

189 Thomas Mudge England 1755
Movement only in brass box. White
enamel dial. Steel beetle hands with centre
seconds hand between hour and minute
hands.
Solid bridge-cock. Two balance-springs,
one with curb compensation and the other
with a regulator. Remontoir with wheel
escaping six times in each revolution, from
anchor-shaped pallets which engage three
teeth of the wheel. The pallets are released
at intervals of one minute by a wheel which
is driven by the remontoir wheel through

187a

187b

187c

189

two springs.
Signed 'Thos Mudge London 260'.
The watch was made for and sold to the
King of Spain on August 22nd 1755.
The brass box was made by George
Daniels who restored the complicated
mechanism to going order in 1967.
Diam 48mm
See also page 7
Presented by John Grant, 1850

190 Gerrit Rensman Holland c1755
Movement only. White enamel dial.
Arcaded minute ring. Pierced gilt hands.
Signed 'Gerrit Rensman Zwol'.
Diam 44mm
Presented by Edwin W. Streeter, 1875

191 Barraud England HM 1756
Silver-gilt pair-case, hallmarked for 1756.
The outer engraved with a floral design,
with some piercing although the watch
neither strikes nor repeats. Both cases are
stamped HG.
Enamel dial. Beetle hands, which are
recent replacements but appropriate to the
watch.
A ribbon in the back plate ornamentation
is signed 'Barraud'.
This watch, is the earliest Barraud clock
or watch so far located, See C. Jagger,
P.P. Barraud (1968) pp 102 & 140 and
plate X. Also the special file in the
Company's library.
Diams 40 and 35mm
Bequeathed by Miss E.M. Barraud, 1972

192 James Cowan Scotland
HM 1757?
Silver pair-case. The outer is unmarked
but stamped HCR. The inner has what looks
like a gothic C but accompanied by a
thistle instead of a cartouche with the
letters HG. 1757 accords with the style of
the watch but a gothic C with a thistle is the
Edinburgh mark for 1834 in which event
the case is not original.
White enamel dial, probably of later date.
Signed 'Jamˢ Cowan, Edinburgh. 398'.
James Cowan, apprenticed 1744, died
1781, is one of the most famous Scottish
makers.
Diams 48 and 42mm
Collinson Collection

193

193 Julien Le Roy France c1760
Gilt case of early nineteenth century.
Stamped AT. Gold dial with ring of white
enamel hour plaques and smaller plaques
for minutes. Diamonds of green
translucent enamel between minute
plaques. Two plaques for name. Dial
winding. Pierced gold hands.
Dumb repeater. Coqueret. Signed 'Jn Le
Roy A Paris' (see number 217).
Diam 45mm
Nelthropp Collection

194 Julien Le Roy France c1760
Silver case, engine-turned with wide cuts.
White enamel dial. Metal centre repoussé
with gilt trophy of arms on green
translucent enamel. The shield is charged
with three fleurs-de-lys and surmounted
by an imperial crown.
Hands later. Coqueret.
Signed 'Jn Le Roy A Paris'.
There were two Julien Le Roys. Numbers
193 and 194 may be by the less famous of
the two.
Diam 48mm
Nelthropp Collection

195 Markwick England
HM 1759–60
Silver pair-case. Both cases with edges and
bezels pierced and chiselled. Stirrup
pendant. Stamped TI. Perhaps not
original. White enamel dial. Beetle hands.
Large balance with fusee arbor for winding
passing through it. No mask on cock.
Clock-watch striking hours and half hours
on bell. Signed 'Markwick London'.
Probably by Robert Markham who was

son-in-law of, and partner with, James
Markwick who died 1730. He used the
names Markwick or Markham in trading,
generally both.
Diams 58 and 48mm
Nelthropp Collection

196 Ferdinand Berthoud France
c1760
Dodecagonal crystal case, faceted, with
gold rim engraved in pattern in blue and
red. Gold bezel with pattern in black, blue,
red and white enamel. Enamelled three-
lobe pendant. White enamel dial. Pierced
gilt hands. Dial winding.
Bridge-cock with coqueret. Pierced plate
covers the whole top plate.
Signed 'Ferdd. Berthoud A Paris'.
Diam 41mm
Nelthropp Collection

197 Andrew Dickie Scotland c1760
Movement only. White enamel dial.
Square pillars.
Signed 'And. Dickie, Edinburgh'.
Diam 38mm
Collinson Collection

198 Henry Hindley England c1760
Silver pair-case, both pierced, possibly
Dutch. Dutch-type dial with arcaded
minute ring. Quarter repeater on bell.
Dust-cap.
Signed 'Hen. Hindley. York' on top plate.
Undoubtedly a genuine Hindley repeating
movement which has been cased or
re-cased in Holland.
Diams 48 and 28mm
Collinson Collection

199 [Julien Le Roy]
France or Switzerland c1760
Movement only. White enamel dial. No
minute figures. Beetle hands set with
diamonds. Dial winding. Signed 'Ju. Le
Roy 13958'.
The signature is wrongly spelt (Ju. instead
of Jn.) and the number is
disproportionately large, so the watch is
probably a Swiss-made forgery.
Diam 35mm
Presented by Samuel E. Atkins, 1875

200 [Julien Le Roy] France c1760
Movement only. No dial.
Oval-shaped bridge. Adjustable potence.
Signed 'Jul. Le Roy A Paris'.
The movement is not numbered. As Le
Roy started numbering his work c1741 and
this movement from its style can hardly be

before 1760 it seems likely to be a forgery.
Also, genuine signatures are 'Julien' or
'Jn.' not 'Jul'.
Diam 39mm
Collinson Collection

201 Benjamin Bulline England
c1765
Pair-case. Inner gilt. Outer painted horn.
White enamel dial. Continental hands.
Cock with looped edge to table. Unusual
'Memento' watch paper.
Signed 'Benj. Bulline, London. 106'.
Diams 52 and 44mm
Collinson Collection

202 J. Stancliffe England HM 1766
Silver pair-case, both hallmarked. Later
pendant. Stamped WB. White enamel dial
signed 'Samuel Appleyeard'. Gold hands.
Top plate covered entirely with silver
decoration.
Signed 'J. Stancliffe. Halifax. 108'.
Diams 51 and 42mm
Collinson Collection

203 Thomas Grignion England
HM 1767–8
Silver pair-case. Outer case covered with
silver-studded leather. Stirrup pendant.
White enamel dial. Steel beetle hands.
Ruby endstone. Signed 'Thos. Grignion
Covt. Garden London 1698'.
Diams 48 and 41mm

204 Willem Writs Holland 1767
Silver triple case. Outer covered
silver-studded shagreen. Inner with glass
back and front. Stirrup pendant. The
silver case is English and has the English
hallmark for 1767. Skeleton dial with extra
glass on which the numerals are painted.
Blued steel pierced hands.
Skeleton top plate, all chiselled. Very small
silver cock. Signed 'Willem Writs
Amsterdam 1767'. Since it agrees with the
hallmark, this number is probably the
date.
Diams 56, 50 and 48mm
Nelthropp Collection

205 Samuel Heydon England
HM 1768
Silver triple case. Inner HM 1768.
Middle HM 1777. Outer covered
tortoiseshell. Inner case stamped RP.
Middle TB.
White enamel dial. Gold spade hands.
Signed 'Saml Heydon. London. 11263'.
Diams 56, 49 and 42mm
Collinson Collection

204a

204b

204c

206 J. Hebert England or Holland
c1770
Gilt pair-case. Outer covered
tortoiseshell. White enamel dial. Gold
pierced hands.
Dutch-type cock with slot to show bob on
balance. Cock table re-engraved with crest
and initials JHM. Signed 'J. Hebert
Brightelmston' (Brighton).
Diams 48 and 41mm
Nelthropp Collection

207 Benjamin Sidey England c1770
Gold pair-case. Outer covered tortoise-
shell. Oval loop pendant. White enamel
dial. No minute figures. Gold arrow hands.
Signed 'B. Sidey London 5083'.
Diams 43 and 38mm
Nelthropp Collection

208 Thomas Hemings England
HM1770–1
Gold pair-case. Outer repoussé in high
relief. White enamel dial. Gold hands.
Diamond endstone. Signed 'Tho.
Hemings London No 825'.
Diams 45 and 38mm
Presented by Mrs Helen M.I.
Cunningham

209 Markwick Markham (Perigal)
England c1770
Silver pair-case, pierced. White enamel
dial signed 'Markwick Markham
Perigal London'.
Engraved cock foot. Quarter repeater.
Movement signed 'Markwick Markham
London 1216'.

This association with Perigal is also found
in watches in the British Museum and
Metropolitan Museum of Art, New York.
He also associated with other makers.
See G. H. Baillie *Watchmakers and
Clockmakers of the World*, also
number 210.
Diam 48mm
Collinson Collection

210 Markwick Markham Borrell
England c1770
Movement only. White enamel dial.
No minute figures. No hands.
Signed 'Markwick Markham Borrell
London 25846'.
See also number 209.
Diam 28mm

211 Thomas Moore England c1770
Single copper case, originally covered but
the covering has gone. White enamel dial.
Continental hands. Signed 'Tho. Moore.
Ipswich'.
This is presumably the Thomas Moore
who invented a fusee to wind both ways,
but this watch has the normal type.
Diam 48mm

212 Isaac Heron America c1770
Movement only. White enamel dial.
Beetle hands. Signed 'Isaac Heron.
New York No. 57'.
This is probably an English-made
movement exported to America, but the
balance-cock at any rate was specially
made, having a heron engraved on it
instead of the usual mark. There is also a

snake engraved round the pivot-hole.
Diam 35mm
Presented by B.L. Vulliamy, 1816

213 Thomas Wagstaff England
HM 1772
Silver-gilt pair-case. Outer repoussé.
White enamel dial. Fleur-de-lys hands
(replacements). Signed 'Thos Wagstaff.
London. 6883'.
The watch has a gold key made of
intertwined wire.
Wagstaff was a Quaker and because of this
members of the Society of Friends from
America used to lodge at his house when
visiting England. This may explain why
several of his clocks and watches are in the
United States. According to Britten one of
Wagstaff's clocks used to be in Kasan
Cathedral, St Petersburg. He worked in
Carey Street and at 33 Gracechurch Street
from 1756 to 1793.
Diams 46 and 40mm
Presented by A. F. Corcoran, 1967

214 John Champion England c1775
Movement only. White enamel dial.
No minute figures. Gold wavy hands.
Dust-cap.
Signed 'Jn. Champion London 1940'.
Diam 35mm
Presented by Evan Roberts, 1904

215 John Arnold England c1776
Single gilt case. Oval loop pendant.
White enamel dial with four subsidiary
dials: above, hours; below, seconds; left,

day of month; right, age of moon. Sweep
minute hand. Gilt hands.
No endstone.
Signed 'J. Arnold London 301'.
Arnold was born 1736, a Freeman of the
Clockmakers' Company 1783, died 1799.
See Vaudrey Mercer, *John Arnold*,
pp 11–12. Mercer records number 227
with HM 1775.
Diam 59mm
Nelthropp Collection

216 Richard Carrington England
HM 1777
Gold pair-case, outer enamelled with the
lion of Scotland. Stamped DA.
Signed 'Richd Carrington. London. 326'.
Diams 43 and 39mm

217 George Goodman England
HM 1778–9?
Gold pair-case, outer engraved with blue
and green enamel in patterns. White
enamel dial. Steel beetle hands.
Signed 'Geo. Goodman. London. 7075'.
Diams 43 and 38mm
Nelthropp Collection

218 J. Millington England c1780
Movement only. Enamel dial. Early type of
narrow pierced cock foot. Square pillars.
Worm set-up. Signed 'J. Millington.
London. 14364'.
Diam 35mm
Collinson Collection

219 Isaac Rogers England HM1780
Quadruple case. Inner pair-case silver,
hallmarked and stamped I.R. Outer case
covered tortoiseshell. Protective outer of
wood, cone-shaped. White enamel dial
with Arabic numerals.
Signed 'Isaac Rogers'.
Pierced gold hands. Movement signed
in Arabic.
The watch has its original carrying cord,
bound and ornamented with silver wire.
Diams outer 70mm, inner 30mm
Bequeathed by M.L. Bateman, 1966

220 J. Wilders [England or
Switzerland] c1780
Movement only. Silver repoussé dial with
arcaded minute ring. Signed in centre.
Square pillars. Ratchet set-up. Bridge-
cock. Signed 'J. Wilders. London. 9290'.
Possibly a Swiss-made watch with an
English signature intended for the Dutch
market.
Diam 36mm
Nelthropp Collection

221 T. Moore England c1780
Pair-case. Gilt inner. Outer covered
tortoiseshell (missing from bezel).
Enamel dial with coloured picture in
centre. No hands.
Movement incomplete.
Signed 'T. Moore. London. 2096'.
Diams 50 and 41mm
Collinson Collection

222 John Nister England c1780
Single gilt case. Back engraved with a
simple design. White enamel dial. Dial
winding. Continental hands
(replacements). Ratchet set-up.
Signed 'Jno Nister. London. N° 407'.
Diam 44mm
Collinson Collection

223 John Wilter [England or Holland]
c1780
Gold pair-case, outer repoussé. Stamped
RRV. Gold dial with arcaded minute ring.
Continental hands. Bridge-cock.
Signed 'John Wilter London' but the lack
of hallmark in a gold case, Continental dial
and hands and bridge-cock suggest Dutch
origin.
Fine English chain, seal and key. The
watch belonged to the Rev Johann
Henricus de Saram, who was the first
Sinhalese to enter the University of
Oxford in 1812. He was sent there by the
Government of Ceylon with a view to his
preaching in Sinhalese on his return to
Ceylon where he was appointed Colonial
Chaplain.
Diams 48 and 44mm
Presented by S.F. de Saram, 1966

224 John Wilter England c1770
Silver pair-case, outer case repoussé and
signed 'Cochin'. Silver champlevé dial,
arcaded minute ring. Aperture for
calendar, Dutch bridge-cock.
Signed 'John Wilter, London'.
Diams 58 and 51mm

225 J. Worke London or Switzerland
c1780
Movement only. Silver repoussé dial with
arcaded minute ring and date aperture.
Signed in centre.
Square pillars. Worm set-up.
Signed 'J. Worke London 9890'.
This movement may be of Swiss
manufacture, given a London signature
and intended for sale in Holland.
Diam 37mm
Nelthropp Collection

226 Jean Antoine Lepine France
c1780
Movement only. White enamel dial.
Gold arrow hands. Screw-adjusted
potence. Hinged cover to movement.
Signed 'Lepine Hger. du Roy a Paris
No. 1612'.
Diam 33mm
Presented by Samuel E. Atkins, 1875

227 Markwick Markham England
HM 1783
Triple case. Two inner of hallmarked
silver. Outer covered tortoiseshell.
Stamped IR. White enamel dial with
Arabic numerals. Steel beetle hands.
Ratchet set-up. Ornate pillars.
Signed 'Markwick Markham. London.
14693' on movement and dial.
Diams 61, 51 and 42mm
Nelthropp Collection

228 Daniel de St Leu England c1785
Movement only. No dial. Engraved cock
foot. Quarter repeater. Round pillars.
Worm set-up. Dust-cap. Signed on
movement and dust-cap
'Dan! De St Leu. Ser^t to her Majesty.
London. 2473'.
Diam 33mm
Presented by George Moore, 1889

229 John Brockbank England c1785
Movement only. White enamel dial.
Steel beetle hands. Signed 'Jno.
Brockbank London 1207'.
Diam 41mm
Presented by Evan Roberts, 1913

230 Samuel Northcote England
c1785
Movement only. Enamel dial signed
'Northcote'.
Narrow engraved cock foot with mask.
Square pillars. The wheels, including
contrate, have six crossings. Signed 'Sam!
Northcote. Plymouth. N° 599'.
Diam 38mm
Presented by Samuel E. Atkins, 1875

231 Robert Best England HM 1787
Pair-case, inner silver-gilt (HM). Outer
gilt-metal. Enamel dial, centre seconds
with subsidiary dials for time, and
regulation. Hour hand broken.
Round pillars. Ratchet set-up. Stop lever
for seconds. Pierced cock. The table with a
medallion vase. Signed 'Rob! Best. Royal
Exchange. London 1470'. Inside the case is
a paper stating 'Bought March 1788.

Given to Christopher May 15th 1818'.
Diams 57 and 50mm
Collinson Collection

232 Gray & Constable England
c1790
Gold case, the back engine-turned and
covered with steel-grey transparent
enamel. Enamelled border and bezel each
set with 35 diamonds. Enamelled oval loop
pendant. White enamel dial. Gold arrow
hands. Steel balance. Signed 'Gray &
Constable London 1251'.
Diam 50mm
See also colour plate II

233 William Plumley England
c1790
Movement only. No dial. Unusual
decorative pillars. Ratchet set-up.
Signed 'Wm Plumley. Ludgate Hill
N.° 5627'.
Diam 35mm

234 Alexander Hare England c1790
Gilt-metal pair-case. Outer stamped 439.
White enamel dial. Beetle hands.
Endstone. Worm set-up.
Signed 'Alex.^r Hare. London. 439'.
Diams 49 and 42mm
Collinson Collection

235 Anonymous Switzerland c1790
Movement only. No dial. Very small oval
movement repeating on a bell, probably
intended for a ring.
Diam 29mm

236 Richard Hoyle England c1790
Gilt-metal pair-case. White enamel dial.
Small subsidiary dial for seconds. Steel
beetle hands.
Cock table with vase medallion; solid
engraved foot. Worm set-up.
Signed 'R.^d Hoyle. London. 1781'.
Diams 53 and 45mm
Presented by Herbert J. Adams, 1910

237 Anonymous France c1790
Movement only, unfinished, but in
working order. Stamped 47 on back plate.
Eight-day movement with two geared
barrels. Dial winding.
Diam 48mm
Presented by Charles Frodsham & Co,
1875

238 Johnson England c1790
Movement only with Continental-type

bridge. Enamel dial. Dial winding. Gold
spade hands. Regulator dial on back plate
is in white enamel. Diamond endstone.
Worm set-up.
Signed 'Johnson. Grays Inn Passage.
909'.
Diam 38mm
Nelthropp Collection

239 James Lamb England c1790
Movement only. No dial.
Silver cock with engraved foot and urn
medallion table. Ratchet set-up.
Signed 'Jam. Lamb. London. N.° 1573'.
Collinson Collection

240 George Goodman England
c1790
Gilt-metal pair-case. Enamel dial.
Stamped IB.
Ratchet set-up. The regulator dial is
engraved on the back plate.
Signed 'Geo. Goodman. London. 2352'.
Diam 47mm
Collinson Collection

241 Eardley Norton England c1790
Silver pair-case. Inner pierced. Enamel
dial. Calendar. Signed 'Eardley Norton
London'.
Quarter repeating movement.
Signed 'Eardley Norton. London. 28847'.
Diam 60mm
Collinson Collection

242 Ann Phillips England c1790
Enamelled case (Staffordshire); the inside
plain white. Outside green, with musical
scene in colours. White enamel dial.
Dial winding. Gold hands.
Solid engraved cock foot. Pierced table.
Signed 'Ann Phillips London 1778'
(1778 is the number, not the date).
Diam 45mm

243 S. Patridge England HM 1792
Silver inner case, the outer missing.
Stamped IW(?) Enamel dial.
Narrow oval table to cock.
Signed 'S. Patridge. London. 1353'.
Diam 49mm
Collinson Collection

244 Thomas Glase England
HM 1794
Silver half-hunter case, of which this is the
earliest example in the collection.
Birmingham hallmark 1794. Stamped HH.
White enamel dial

Signed 'Thos Glase. Bridgnorth 252'.
Diam 53mm
Bequeathed by T. Vickery, 1946

245 Green & Ward England c1795
Pair-case. Outer gilt, covered shagreen.
Inner engine-turned gold covered
translucent blue enamel. Rims of white
enamel with gold wreath on blue enamel.
Similar rim on bezel.
Cock table with wheel ornamentation.
Signed 'Green & Ward London
No. 2122'. With short chain and key.
Diams 53 and 48mm
Presented by Sir Robert M. Jackson Bt,
1934

246 Ch. Moricand Switzerland
c1795
Movement only. Enamel dial. In poor
condition, of interest only because of its
small size.
Signed 'Ch.^t Moricand a Geneve'.
Diam 20mm
Collinson Collection

242a

242b

247 Isaac Rogers England HM 1795
Unused and unfinished watch.
Triple case, metal outer, two inner silver.
The outer case was clearly intended to be
covered with some material such as
tortoiseshell but this was never
completed. Inner case HM 1796 and
stamped JC. Middle case HM 1795 and
stamped WI. The recess in the outer case to
receive the pendant is wrongly placed
compared with the recess to take the hinge
of the middle case. This mistake would be
difficult to correct and it may be that for
this reason the watch was put on one side
and never finished.
Enamel dial. Gold arrow hands.
Cock table pierced with Prince of Wales
feathers. Dust-cap cut away to show the
cock. Ratchet set-up.
Signed 'Isaac Rogers. London 20065'.
Very similar to number 248.
Diams 71, 59 and 49mm

248 Isaac Rogers England HM 1796
Pair-case. Inner silver, stamped JC/T.
Hallmarked 1796. Outer covered
tortoiseshell with pinwork, incomplete.
White enamel dial. Polished steel beetle
hands.
Cock table pierced with Prince of Wales
feathers. Dust-cap cut away to show the
cock.
Signed 'Isaac Rogers. London 20068'.
This watch is almost identical to number
247 and equally unblemished apart from
some damage to the outer case.
Diams 59 and 50mm

249 Daniel de St Leu England
HM 1797-8
Gold pair-case. Outer case has an
engraved trophy of arms surrounding
five crescents. Edge and bezel pierced.
Inner engraved and pierced. Oval loop
pendant. Stamped IW. White enamel dial.
No minute figures. Signed 'De St. Leu
London'. Gold hands with looped stems.
Ruby endstone. Engraved plaque on top
plate. Clock-watch striking on bell, with
strike-silent lever. Signed 'Danl. De St.
Leu. Watch Maker to her Majesty
London 3861'.
Short double chain and cast and engraved
key.
Diams 71 and 64mm
Presented by Sir David Salomons Bt, 1921

250 Benjamin Webb England
HM 1799
Silver pair-case. Stamped NTW. White
enamel dial. Subsidiary dials for hours and
minutes at III position. Seconds at VI.

Compass at IX. Signed on movement and
dial 'Ben. Webb. London No. 129. By the
King's Patent'.
Diams 60 and 55mm

251 Jean Antoine Lepine France
2nd half 18th century
Pair-case. The outer consists of gilt
bezels with glass. Inner gold case has back
enamelled with portrait in oval gold
engraved rim with enamel ornaments.
Outside is a broad band of black enamel
with green and gold wreaths. Edge and
bezel engraved.
White enamel dial. Gold pierced hands.
Dial winding.
Lens-shaped cock with coqueret.
Screw-adjusted potence.
Signed 'Lepine a Paris'.
Diams 48 and 43mm
Presented by John W. Carter, 1896

252 Rosomans England
2nd half 18th century
Gilt pair-case. Outer enamelled with a
portrait in an oval border of white and gold
on dark blue. White enamel dial. No
minute figures. Gold spade hands.
Signed 'Rosomans London 506'.
Diams 45 and 38mm

253 French England
Late 18th century
Triple gilt case. Outer covered
tortoiseshell. Middle and inner plain.
White enamel dial. Turkish numerals.
Steel beetle hands. Signed 'French Royal
Exchange London 22247'.
Probably by Edward French, a Freeman of
the Clockmakers' Company 1782.
Died 1822.
Diams 58, 50 and 43mm
Nelthropp Collection

254 Daniel de St Leu England
Late 18th century
Gold case enamelled on back with a
pastoral scene. Bezel with enamel
plaques. Signed 'Danl De St Leu Sert. to
her Majesty London 1105'.
Diam 45mm
Nelthropp Collection

255 Marchand fils France
Late 18th century
Gilt case covered tortoiseshell. Oval loop
pendant. White enamel dial. Gold hands
set with pearls. Dial winding.
French cock and coqueret.
Signed 'Marchand fils A Paris 33220'.

With silver chatelaine and seals.
Diam 35mm
Nelthropp Collection

256 Charles Ducomun Switzerland
Late 18th century
Movement only. White enamel dial.
Hour ring below. Aperture above with
sun as pointer to show times of sunrise and
sunset. The aperture is progressively
closed and opened by shutters to show the
hours of daylight. Small dials left and right
show month and date. Dial winding.
Coqueret.
Signed 'Cles. Ducomun dit Boudrile'.
Diam 50mm
Presented by B.L. Vulliamy, 1848

257 Anonymous Late 18th century
Gold pair-case. Inner has a lake scene in
enamel *à l'aurore*. Bezel studded with
diamonds. White enamel dial. No minute
figures. Gold hands. Repeater.
Diams 45 and 38mm
Nelthropp Collection

258 Eardley Norton England
Late 18th century
Silver case. White enamel dial with gold
spade hands.
Engraved silver dust-cap and engraved top
plate. Wheel cock of bridge type.
Signed 'Eardley Norton London'.
Diam 48mm
Presented by William Barnsdale, 1906

259 Chevalier l'aîné France
Late 18th century
Gilt case. Back enamelled with a country
scene. White enamel dial. No minute
figures. Dial winding. Gold fleurs-de-lys
hands.
French cock and coqueret.
Signed 'Chevalier l'aîné'.
Diam 56mm
Nelthropp Collection

260 Thomas Wright England
Late 18th century
Gilt pair-case. Oval loop pendant. White
enamel dial. Gold arrow hands. Cock has a
crown, and below on a ribbon 'Wright
Watchmaker to the King'. Signed 'Wright
in the Poultry London No. 3052'.
Wright was a Freeman of the Clockmakers'
Company 1770. Died 1792.
Diams 48 and 41mm
Presented by W.K. Bowen, 1901

261 James McCabe England
Late 18th century
Movement only. White enamel dial.
No minute figures.
Signed 'James McCabe London 5020'.
McCabe was a Freeman of the
Clockmakers' Company 1781, became
Senior Warden and died 1811.
Diam 46mm
Presented by T.W. Jones, 1915

262 Ecklicot Late 18th century
Forgery of John Ellicott. Signed 'Ecklicot,
London'. Movement only.
Diam 36mm

263 Robert Robin France
Late 18th century
Gilt case. Back with painted enamel figure
scene. White enamel dial. No minute
figures. Gold arrow hands. Dial winding.
Signed 'Robert Robin Paris'.
Diam 53mm
Nelthropp Collection

264 Anonymous Switzerland
Early 19th century
Gold case enamelled in a lakeland scene
with border of pearls. Bezel has a border of
pearls. Matt gold dial. White enamel hour
plaques and minute band. Steel looped
hands. Dial winding.
Bridge-cock.
Diam 36mm
Nelthropp Collection

265 Anonymous Switzerland
Early 19th century
Gold case. Engine-turned covered with
translucent blue enamel, with a border of
pearls. White enamel dial. Steel looped
hands. Dial winding.
Diam 28mm
Nelthropp Collection

266 Yeriaf (Fairey) [Switzerland]
Early 19th century
Case in four-colour gold set with
turquoises and garnets. Engine-turned
gold dial with floral border and polished
hour ring.
Bridge-cock and coqueret.
Signed 'Yeriaf' (Fairey spelt backwards).
Diam 41mm
Nelthropp Collection

267 Anonymous Switzerland or
France c1800
Gold case. Dial with white enamel hour
ring and central gold plaque engraved with

figure scene.
Narrow bridge-cock with steel coqueret.
Musical and repeating movement.
Diam 56mm
Presented by Sir Cecil Bigwood, 1948

268 J. Joseph England c1800
Pair-case. Outer case covered leather piqué
gold in a simple pattern c1725. Inner case
and movement c1800.
Signed 'J. Joseph Bristol'.
Diams 38 and 33mm
Nelthropp Collection

268

269 Anonymous [France] c1800
Gold pair-case. Outer covered shagreen.
Inner case engine-turned. Dial winding.
White enamel dial and hands
replacements.
Bridge-cock with coqueret.
Diams 56 and 48mm
Nelthropp Collection

270 Philippe Terrot Switzerland
c1800
Silver case in form of a cockle-shell.
White enamel dial. Gold spade hands.
Dial winding.
Coqueret. Screw-adjusted potence.
Movement and dial signed 'Phe. Terrot
a Geneve 19790'.
Length 55mm

271 Edward Prior England c1800
Four silver cases. The outer conical
dome-shaped, 33mm high. The next
covered tortoiseshell piqué silver. The
inner two plain.
White enamel dial with Turkish numerals.
Gold beetle hands. Signed 'Edwd. Prior
London 45692'.
Diams 71, 61, 53 and 43mm

272 Anonymous Switzerland or
France c1800
Silver case with glass back and front.
White enamel dials, back and front.
Eccentric white hour dial with cherubs on
yellow ground below, and regulator dial.
Steel hands. The back has an enamel dial
for calendar, with outer ring for day of
week and inner ring for day of month. Two
steel hands.
Diam 36mm
Nelthropp Collection

273 Phillipe Terrot Switzerland
c1800
Gilt case. Enamel figure scene on back.
Oval loop pendant. White enamel dial.
Steel loop hands. Dial winding.
Coqueret. Signed 'Ph. Terrot à Genève'.
Diam 53mm

274 Ralph Gout England c1800
Combined watch and pedometer. Gilt
case. Skeleton dial with four enamel
circles. Above for hours and minutes.
On right for steps up to 10. On left up to
100 steps. Large central circle up to
10,000 steps. Gout patented his invention
in 1791 in two forms, number 1 and
number 2. This is an example of
number 2. Combined watches and
pedometers are rare.
See Woods, *Curiosities of Clocks and
Watches* (1866), p.348 and Clutton &
Daniels, *Watches* (1965), figs.416–17.
Movement with dust-cap and diamond
endstone.
Signed 'Ralph Gout. London. 202'.
Diam 54mm
Nelthropp Collection

275 Ralph Gout England c1800
Combined watch and pedometer.
Signed 'Ralph Gout. London. 267. By the
King's letters patent'.
This is virtually identical with number 274
above, qv.
Diam 54mm
Presented by G.S. Sanders

276 Terrot & Fazy   Switzerland
c1800
Engraved gold case. White enamel dial.
Gold looped hands. Dial winding.
Coqueret. Signed 'Terrot & Fazy A
Genève'.
Diam 31mm
Nelthropp Collection

277 Anonymous   [Russia]   c1800
Boxwood case. Boxwood dial. Ivory hands.
Dial winding.
Wood plates and cock. Cock has large foot
and coqueret with jewel. Centre, third and
contrate wheel of ivory.
Diam 56mm
Presented by Louis Dee, 1883

278 James Keene   England
Dated 1800
Silver pair-case. Both hallmarked 1799
(Birmingham). Both are stamped WR and
engraved with the letters JK. Enamel dial
painted with the (incorrect) arms of the
Weavers' Company.
The cock does not cover the balance.
Signed 'James Keene A.D.1800
Liverpool'.
Diams 57 and 49mm
Collinson Collection

279 George Flote   England   c1800
Pair-case. Inner gilt. Outer covered horn
with arms of Clockmakers' Company.
Stamped IM. Enamel dial.
Round pillars.
Signed 'Geo. Flote London 1790'.
Diams 52 and 44mm
Bequeathed by Miss Isobel Webster, 1966

280 James Williams   England   c1800
Gilt pair-case with watchpapers of
Madras and Calcutta. Stamped TG.
Enamel dial overlapping hour-minute
ring.
Round pillars.
Signed 'Jas Williams. Bath. 1602'.
Diams 58 and 51mm
Collinson Collection

281 Girardier   Switzerland   c1800
Silver case. Stamped AIDC 10883. Gilt
and silver dial containing small dial for
hours and minutes also secret panel and
two plaques.
Bridge-cock.
Signed 'Girardier l'aîné No 11405'.
Charles Girardier of Geneva was
awarded a prize in 1792 by the Société des
Arts.

Diam 54mm
Collinson Collection

282 Grant   England   c1800
Silver case, a replacement, hallmarked
1863.
Dial, eccentric hour ring overlapping
seconds circle.
Dust-cap signed 'Grant. Fleet Street,
London. 1571'. Probably the elder Grant
who made number 461, which is
numbered 2802 and hallmarked 1804.
Diam 57mm
Collinson Collection

283 Willeumier Frères   Switzerland
HM 1801–2
Silver case, engine-turned (English).
White enamel dial, gold loop hands.
Dial winding.
Bridge-cock. Ruby endstone. Eight-day
movement with two mainsprings geared
together, with the fusee chain round one.
Signed 'Willeumier Frères à Tramelan'.
Diam 61mm
Nelthropp Collection

284 James Lawson   England
HM 1802
Silver pair-case, both hallmarked and
stamped RG. Enamel dial. Gold arrow
hands.
Round pillars. Ratchet set-up.
Engraved cock foot with mask.
Signed 'Jas Lawson. London 1870'.
Diams 52 and 46mm
Collinson Collection

285 John Grant   England
HM 1803–4
Silver pair-case. Oval loop pendant.
White enamel dial. Gold spade hands.
Ruby endstone. Hour repeater by turning
the pendant as far as it will go and
counting the ticks during its return.
Signed 'J.G. London 1804'.
Diams 61 and 54mm
Presented by his son, John Grant, 1874

286 F. Atkin   England   HM 1807
Silver pair-case, both hallmarked.
White enamel dial with 'Henry Boxwell'
instead of numerals. Chester hallmark.
Signed 'F. Atkin, Wexford, 332'.
Diams 56 and 49mm
Presented by Mrs Boxwell, 1962

287 Wightwick & Moss   England
c1806

Gold case. Back of translucent blue enamel
with ring of pearls. In centre, plaited hair
under glass, with ring of diamonds. Bezel
with blue enamel and ring of pearls.
The chatelaine has blue enamel bars with
white borders, studded diamonds,
joined by triple strings of pearls, with fob
hook. Stamped VW.
White enamel dial. Gold arrow hands.
Dial winding. Signed 'Wightwick & Moss
Ludgate St. London 2776'.
The watch was given by the second Lord
Nelson to Sir Jonathan Miles, Sheriff of
London, 1806.
Wightwick was a Freeman of the
Clockmakers' Company c1781.
Diam 48mm
Presented by the Rt Hon Viscount
Wakefield of Hythe, 1931
See also colour plate II

288 William Bower   England
Probably 1808
Pair-case of pinchbeck metal. White
enamel dial with hour and seconds
circles intersecting.
Cock, bust of Nelson and 'NELSON' below.
Dust cap. Signed 'William Bower
Chesterfield 1808'.
Diams 55 and 50mm
Presented by Sir Robert M. Jackson Bt,
1934

289 Francis Atkins   England
Probably 1808
Movement only. Steel balance. Signed
'Francis Atkins London 3659'.
Atkins was born 1730, admitted to the
Clockmakers' Company 1759, Master
1780, died 1809. He was also Clerk of the
Company 1785–1809. Presented by his
grandson, Samuel E. Atkins, who had
probably been told by his grandfather
that he made the movement in 1808.
Diam 41mm

290 Barrauds   England   c1810
Silver pair-case, known to be a
replacement in 1969 and hallmarked 1827.
White enamel dial signed 'Barrauds
6863'.
Plain brass balance and cock. Signed on
back plate 'Barrauds Cornhill London
6863'.
Diams 55 and 48mm
Bequeathed by Miss E.M. Barraud, 1972,
with a silver chain

291 Jean Robert Soret   Switzerland
HM 1812–13
Gold case. Engine-turned. Dial

enamelled with a lake scene. Four-colour gold foreground with automaton figures on a see-saw. The sky is enamelled black with two gold cherubs striking bells. Very small central white enamel dial. Bridge-cock. with coqueret. Oil sinks. Quarter repeating and moving the figures on the dial. Signed 'Jn. Robert Soret à Genève. 33411'.
Diam 50mm
Presented by John W. Carter, 1899
See also colour plate IV

292 **James McCabe**　England
HM 1813–14
Gold engine-turned case. Pendant with spiral-shaped knob.
White enamel dial. Gold serpentine hands.
Diamond endstone. Signed 'Jas. McCabe Royal Exchange London 7779'.
Diam 45mm
Nelthropp Collection

293 **Edward Prior**　England
HM 1814
Silver pair-case. Stamped IR. Enamel dial signed 'Edward Prior London'.
Minute hand broken.
Pierced cock table and foot and ornamentation to back plate. Pierced pillars.
Signed 'Edwd Prior London 39405'.
Diams 61 and 50mm
Collinson Collection

294 **Charles Edward Viner**　England
HM 1815–16
Silver engine-turned case. White enamel dial. Gold spade hands. The hand for the alarm is set by turning the pendant (Viner's patent). Alarm. Ruby endstone.
Signed 'Viner London Royal Exchange & New Bond Street Patent No. 569'.
Viner was a Freeman of the Clockmakers' Company 1815.
Diam 57mm
Nelthropp Collection

295 **Bordier**　Switzerland　c1815
Silver (?) case. Dome pierced for alarm.
Stamped FRT.1534.
Enamel dial. Two ringed winding-holes and alarm hand. Signed 'Bordier a Geneve No. 3658'.
Diam 56mm
Collinson Collection

296 **Grayhurst & Harvey**　England
c1815
Silver hunter case. Hallmark illegible.

Enamel dial. Diamond-ended gold hands.
Cock with endstone and gargoyle mask.
Signed 'Grayhurst & Harvey, Strand. 2723'.
Diam 58mm
Collinson Collection

297 **Thomas Farr**　England　1816
Gold case. Gold dial with raised hour figures and engine-turned centre.
Seconds dial with engine-turned centre.
Four-colour gold wreath round dial.
Gold spade hands.
Diamond endstone.
Signed 'Thos. Farr. Bristol'.
Diam 56mm
Nelthropp Collection

298 **Lormier**　England　HM 1817
Silver pair-case, both hallmarked.
Stamped ML. Enamel dial. Seconds dial.
Stop-start lever. Signed 'Lormier, Shoreditch. No 1284'.
Diams 58 and 52mm
Collinson Collection

299 **Alexander & Co**　England　c1820
Silver hunter case. Modern type of pendant. White enamel dial. Seconds dial.
Gold spade hands.
Ruby endstone. Dust-cap. Has a cross-stitch pad 'Prepare to meet thy God 1882'.
Signed 'Alexander & Co London no 1361'.
Diam 56mm
Presented by Robert Marsland, 1918

300 **Thomas Glase**　England
HM 1820
Silver pair-case, the outer half-hunter.
Birmingham hallmark 1820. Stamped HH.
Enamel dial with inner hour ring.
Signed 'Thos Glase Bridgnorth'.
Diam 54mm
Bequeathed by T. Vickery, 1946

301 **George Prior**　England　HM 1815
Triple silver cases, outer oyster shaped.
Framed dial with Turkish numerals.
Signed 'Ge Prior. 5345'.
Diams 75, 64 and 54mm
Presented by Miss Victoria Leveson Gower, 1969

302 **John Bloor**　England　HM 1827
Silver pair-case with half-hunter inner.
Both with Birmingham hallmark.
Stamped JH. Enamel dial, double chapter for half-hunter. Signed 'John Bloor Newcastle. No.578'.

Diams 54 and 48mm
Presented by John Byram, 1963

303 **Anonymous**　Switzerland　c1830
Silver case. Stamped 'AJ.1459'. Enamel dial with alarm hand. The alarm is set by twisting a small disc at top of the fixed pendant.
Diam 35mm
Collinson Collection

304 **Markwick Markham**　England
HM 1835
Triple silver case, middle plain, outer covered tortoiseshell and pinwork.
Stamped IR. Enamel dial signed 'Markwick Markham London'. Beetle hands. Signed 'Markwick Markham London 19504'.
A new unused watch.
Diams 70, 60 and 48mm
Bequeathed by M.L. Bateman, 1966

305 **Edward Prior**　England
HM 1838
Silver pair-case both hallmarked.
Stamped JD. Enamel dial with Arabic numerals and signed 'Edward Prior, London'. (The decoration surrounding the signature appears not to be original.)
Signed 'Edwd Prior London 4973'.
Diams 46 and 36mm
Collinson Collection

306 **P. James Evans**　England
HM 1838
Silver pair-case, both hallmarked.
'MH' engraved on back. Enamel dial.
Signed 'P. Jas Evans. Sherwsbury' (sic) '2212'.
Diams 48 and 42mm
Bequeathed by T. Vickery, 1946

307 **William Allman**　England　c1840
Pair-case of white metal. Enamel dial.
Flat steel balance.
Signed 'Wm Allman. Woolwich. No 920'.
Diams 54 and 48mm
Collinson Collection

308 **Anonymous**　Switzerland　c1850
Gold spherical case enamelled in a scene of bird feeding its young (covers are badly crushed). White enamel. Gold hands.
Dial winding. Signed 'No.4993'.
Diam 22mm
Nelthropp Collection

309 **Simon Nicolet**　Switzerland
c1850

Silver case stamped K6739. Enamel dial
signed 'Simon Nicolet' with alarm-set
hand. Signed 'Simon Nicolet'.
Diam 54mm
Collinson Collection

310 **Anonymous** England c1850
Movement only. Gold dial, centre
engraved. Gold hands.
Diam 38mm
Presented by John W. Carter, 1904

311 **Anonymous** England HM 1854
Silver pair-case, both hallmarked and
numbered 8150 and stamped $\frac{2}{10}$ BK.
Birmingham hallmark. Engraved brass
dial plate with engraved motto round
circumference 'Keep me clean and use me
well and I to you the truth will tell'.
Superimposed enamel chapter ring.
Diams 58 and 51mm
Collinson Collection

312 **James McCabe** England
HM 1857
Silver engine-turned case stamped JJ.
Enamel dial.
Cock with round table. Signed 'James
McCabe, London 2505'.
Diam 46mm
Collinson Collection

313 **Anonymous** England HM 1860
Silver pair-case. Inner numbered 44893.
Stamped PW.
Diams 56 and 48mm
Collinson Collection

Watches with cylinder escapement

The cylinder escapement has gone through four main stages in its history spreading over roughly two hundred years. The original idea occurred to Thomas Tompion at the end of the seventeenth century, although his version was more like a virgule than a true cylinder escapement. In any case he does not seem to have developed it and no example has survived. The true cylinder escapement was evolved by George Graham in about 1725, although specimens before about 1740 are rare. Graham's cylinder was made of steel with an escape-wheel of brass and it continued with only minor refinements for fifty years. The next stage was a ruby cylinder with a steel escape-wheel and it was introduced by the leading British makers in the 1770s. It had the merit of being very much more durable than the steel cylinder, where particles of dust became embedded in the brass teeth of the escape-wheel and rapidly cut through the steel. The ruby version was, indeed, almost indestructible by wear, but it was exceedingly fragile and prone to breakage by shock. The consequent repair was at any time expensive and today would be virtually impossible. The third stage came from Breguet who took a ruby cylinder and mounted it on an overhung cranked extension of the balance-staff. The ruby, therefore, formed no part of the balance-staff and was not prone to breakage in almost any circumstances; the more so as the staff was mounted between Breguet's spring-mounted 'parachutes'. Finally came the almost mass-produced cheap Swiss cylinder watches, which took advantage of the escapement to make possible a very thin movement and were popular throughout the nineteenth century.

The oldest cylinder escapement in the Collection, appropriately, is by Graham (catalogue number 314). It survives only as a movement and may be dated at about 1735; but only a little later is a watch by the almost unknown London maker Thomas Day (catalogue number 315). With catalogue number 316 (illustrated) we are on surer dating ground since the gold pair-case is hallmarked for 1739. It has all the usual Graham characteristics, such as his very elegant enamel dial; blued steel hands, and polished steel centre seconds hand placed between the hour and minute hands. The movement has the solid engraved cock foot found in all but a few very early Graham watches, and an endstone mounted in a steel setting. All these are shown clearly in the illustration and were adhered to by Graham throughout his life and afterwards by Mudge.

It is interesting, although logical, that Graham's simple watches are larger by two millimetres than his more complicated repeaters. His repeaters were very expensive and he evidently felt that despite their greater complication they should be smaller than the simple watches. They were invariably quarter repeaters, striking on a bell, and they do not have a seconds hand. Catalogue number 317 (illustrated) is an exceptionally fine example, hallmarked 1745, and the outer case is covered with leather, studded with gold pins. Catalogue number 322, a gold watch hallmarked 1751, must be one of the very last made in Graham's lifetime and its number, 6543, is believed to be the latest recorded number by him.

Scotland is represented by a movement by the Edinburgh maker Andrew Dickie, of about 1750 (catalogue number 324).

Unusual in having a skeleton movement is number 325 (illustrated), a silver-gilt watch by Lawrence of Bath, hallmarked 1763. Catalogue number 331, a movement of about 1770 by Samuel Toulmin has a pirouette attachment – an arrangement used by Huygens for his first balance-spring watches in order to give the balance-wheel a more lively action than the 100° arc of an ordinary verge escapement – though it is hard to see what good it could do for a cylinder.

316a

316b

Josiah Emery was one of the first makers to use a ruby cylinder and an early example of his work, dating perhaps from 1775, is a movement here illustrated, catalogue number 335, and there is another, similar movement by him, catalogue number 350. Both have compensation curbs consisting of two bi-metallic strips and are very similar to watches by Perigal and other early precision makers. This suggests that there was a close link between this small band of pioneers and that most of their ébauches may have been made by the same man, perhaps Richard Pendleton.

Although Breguet used his version of the ruby cylinder escapement more frequently than anything else he did not arrive at it until the mid 1790s, before which he was content to use a plain steel cylinder. His work from before the French Revolution is exceedingly rare and the Collection is fortunate in possessing two very early and important examples, both with ordinary steel cylinders. Both have the system of fractional numbering used by Breguet prior to 1787, of which barely half a dozen survive. They are illustrated, catalogue numbers 347 and 348. Number 347 has the marking $8\frac{10}{83}$ which is interpreted to mean that it is his eighth watch and was completed in October 1783. It has the added importance of being self-winding, or in Breguet's terms, a '*montre perpetuelle*'. Breguet is known to have made a perpetuelle in 1782, but it does not seem to have survived, so that this watch is almost certainly the oldest surviving Breguet perpetuelle. There is one reputedly made in 1780, for the Duc d'Orléans, but a great deal of mystery surrounds it, and by virtue of its sophisticated design and execution and its lever escapement it certainly was not made before the Revolution. Number 347 by contrast is of quite crude execution which really does Breguet no great amount of credit and is quite unlike his mature work. In addition to being a perpetuelle it is a quarter repeater on wire gongs. The dial and hands are not typical of Breguet's earliest work and may well be later replacements by him, as almost certainly is the gold case, which bears the letter N surmounted by a crown. The watch reputedly belonged to the Grand Duke Nicholas, later Czar Nicholas I of Russia.

The second Breguet of this class is number $128\frac{5}{85}$ (catalogue number 348). This has a perfectly plain and not very distinguished cylinder movement such as many French or Swiss makers for the trade were turning out in the 1780s, fitted with a very high-quality minute-repeating train. The implication here is that, in his early days, Breguet was content, or had perforce, to use trade movements. But evidently he was not proud of the fact as he made it very difficult for anyone to see the movement. His signature is on the dust-cap but this can only be removed by removing first the hands and dial and then lifting the movement out of the case. The dial of this watch is a mystery since, although it has a perfectly creditable Breguet signature typical of the pre-Revolution watches, the Roman numerals, gold beetle and poker hands are typically English.

Breguet's ruby cylinder escapement is contained in two of his *montres à souscription*, catalogue numbers 368 and 371, both of which are illustrated. It is, in fact, impossible ever to see a Breguet ruby cylinder without removing the dial, since it is always mounted between the back plate and the dial. Catalogue number 368 has the very early number, for a *souscription* watch, of 518, placing it at about 1800. It has the ugly triangular-shaped hand occasionally found in this type of watch, whose sole merit was that it was much less fragile than the very fine and elegant typical *souscription* hand found in the later *souscription*, catalogue number 371 (Breguet's number 1411 places it not earlier than 1805). The movements of both watches are almost identical so that only number 368 is illustrated. The dial of number 371 is unusual if not unique among *souscriptions* in that the usual 5-minute divisions of the *souscription* dials are further subdivided into units of $2\frac{1}{2}$ minutes. Another perpetuelle cylinder watch, dating from about 1800, is catalogue number 367, by Berthoud.

Particularly interesting and elegant is catalogue number 364, illustrated in colour. Although only 18mm in diameter it has an extra wheel in the train and goes for 8 days. It was made by Milleret and Tissot of Switzerland and has an elegant enamelled chain.

Coteau was a renowned painter of enamel clock and watch dials, and dials signed by him are greatly prized. Two are found on one watch, catalogue number 340, by Gautrin. This watch has complicated calendar-work demanding a dial on both sides of the watch.

An early example of Lepine's calibre, with separate cocks, is found in a movement by Lepine himself, catalogue number 355.

The cylinder escapement was often combined with musical boxes in the early nineteenth century. The musical trains are invariably of Swiss manufacture, but one is found combined with an English watch by McCabe (catalogue number 366).

The last serious appearance of the cylinder escapement in British watches was in the very superior keyless-wound watches of John Roger Arnold. His foreman, Thomas Prest, took out a patent for keyless winding in 1820 and Arnold employed it in a number of ruby cylinder watches with 'sugar-tongs' compensation curbs. They generally had matt gold dials with applied, polished gold numerals and a typical example is illustrated, catalogue number 378. It is hallmarked for 1821. In these watches the hands still had to be set with a key, and the keyless hand-setting mechanism did not appear until 1850.

An example of the very thin Swiss cylinder watches is catalogue number 389, from the end of the nineteenth century and the latest specimens of this escapement in the Collection, catalogue numbers 390 and 391, are of about 1900. The latter is a *montre mystérieuse*, where there appears to be no connection between the movement and the hands which are set in a transparent dial.

Cylinder escapement

314 George Graham England c1735
Movement only. No dial. Quarter-repeater. Solid engraved cock foot. Signed 'Geo. Graham London 632' (Number repeated under cock foot) Diam 35mm
See also page 41
Bequeathed by T. Vickery, 1946

315 Thomas Day England c1730
Gold pair-case, not original. Outer covered tortoiseshell. White enamel dial with seconds markings. Centre seconds. Endstone. Mechanism to stop and start the centre seconds. From this, and a painting on fabric in the back of the outer case of Aesculapius it may be supposed that the watch belonged to a doctor. It is probably the earliest cylinder, and centre-seconds watch in the collection, although dating it is difficult.
Signed 'Thomas Day London'.
A Thomas Day was made a Freeman of the Clockmakers' Company in 1691.
Diams 47 and 41mm
See also page 41

316 George Graham England
HM 1739–40
Silver pair-case. Stirrup pendant. Stamped I.W. White enamel dial. Steel beetle hands. Centre seconds hand between hour and minute hands. Diamond endstone. Signed dust-cap. Stop lever acting on pin on balance arbor. Signed 'Geo. Graham London 5863'. Graham was born 1673, a Freeman of the Clockmakers' Company 1695, Master 1722, died 1751.
Diams 50 and 43mm
See also page 41
Illustrated on page 41

317a

317b

317c

317 George Graham England
HM 1745–6
Gold pair-case. Outer and bezel covered
leather, studded gold. Inner with edge
pierced and engraved. Stirrup pendant.
White enamel dial. Steel beetle hands.
Diamond endstone. Signed dust-cap.
Quarter repeater on bell.
Signed 'Geo. Graham London 883'.
Diams 48 and 41mm
See also page 41

318 George Graham England
HM 1746–7
Pair-case, outer gilt, covered tortoiseshell.
Inner gold. Stirrup pendant. White
enamel dial, not original. Gold beetle
hands.
Diamond endstone.
Signed dust-cap.
Signed 'Geo. Graham. London. 6270'.
With cut steel chain and keys.
Diams 50 and 43mm
Presented by John W. Carter, 1898

319 Conyers Dunlop England
Mid 18th century
Gold case enamelled with a classical
subject by G.M. Moser in gold frame.
Engraved bezel. Stirrup pendant. White
enamel dial. Steel beetle hands.
Dial winding.
Ruby endstone. Rim cap. Top plate
engraved. Cock with pierced table and
solid engraved foot. Dumb repeater.
Signed 'Conrs Dunlop London 3383'.
Dunlop was a Freeman of the
Clockmakers' Company 1733, Master
1758, died 1779.
Diam 50mm
See also colour plate IV

320 Gray & Vulliamy England
Mid 18th century
Gold pair-case. Outer covered shagreen.
Stamped JR or TR. White enamel dial.
Steel beetle hands.
Ruby endstone. Signed 'Benj. Gray Just.
Vulliamy. London n.n.s.'.
Benjamin Gray was clockmaker to
George II. Justin Vulliamy was his
son-in-law.
Diams 48 and 40mm
Presented by B.L. Vulliamy, 1853

321 Thomas Mudge England c1750
Movement only, no dial. Quarter
repeater. Signed on movement and
dust-cap 'Thos. Mudge, London 481'.
Diam 32mm
Collinson Collection

322 George Graham England
HM 1751–2
Gold pair-case. Outer covered
tortoiseshell with inlaid monogram and
crown. White enamel dial. Blued steel
beetle hands. Polished steel centre
seconds hand between hour and minute
hands. Stop lever.
Diamond endstone. Signed on movement
and dust-cap.
Signed 'Geo. Graham London 6543'.
This watch was bought at the Sir W.
Knighton sale on May 21st 1885. He was
physician and Private Secretary to
George IV.
Diams 50 and 43mm
See also page 41
Nelthropp Collection

323 William Allam England
Mid 18th century
Movement only. White enamel dial.
Steel beetle hands. Centre seconds.
Diamond endstone. Stop lever.
Dust-cap. Signed 'Willm. Allam
London. No. 1030'.
Diam 35mm
Nelthropp Collection

324 Andrew Dickie Scotland
Mid 18th century
Movement only. White enamel dial.
Centre seconds.
Cylinder with pirouette escapement.
Dust-cap. Signed 'Andrew Dickie
Edinburgh'.
Probably made for a box or walking-stick
handle.
Diam 41mm
Nelthropp Collection

325 Lawrence England HM 1763–4
Silver-gilt case engraved on back. Oval
loop pendant. White enamel dial. Steel
beetle hands. Dial winding.
Steel balance-wheel with diamond
endstone. Skeleton top plate, barrel
cover with spokes to show spring. Back
cover with glass. Signed 'Lawrence Bath'.
The case contains a lace watch-paper with
the initials G.H. worked in hair.
Diam 48mm
See also page 41
Nelthropp Collection

326 Thomas Fludgate England
c1765
Movement only. No dial.
Escape wheel perhaps gold. Dust-cap
Foliate pillars. Signed 'Thos Fludgate
2947' on back plate and dust-cap.

Diam 37mm
Presented by Evan Roberts, 1904

327 Thomas Grignion England
HM 1766–7
Gold pair-case repeater. Both cases
pierced and engraved. Stirrup pendant.
White enamel dial. Steel beetle hands.
Ruby endstone.
Signed 'Thos. Grignion London 1464'.
Diams 48 and 43mm
Presented by John W. Carter, 1912

328 John Ellicott & Son England
HM 1767–8
Gold pair-case. Outer repoussé in high
relief and signed 'Manly F.'.
White enamel dial and gold hands
replacements.
Diamond endstone. Dust-cap.
Signed 'Ellicott London 6027'.
Diams 48 and 41mm

329 John Leroux England c1767–8
Movement only. White enamel dial
signed 'Leroux Charing Cross'. Steel
hands. Half-quarter repeater. Dust-cap.
Signed 'J. Leroux London 2607'.
Leroux was a Freeman of the Clockmakers'
Company 1781. The movement may be
dated fairly precisely by reference to other
numbered movements in hallmarked
cases.
Diam 48mm
Presented by T.W. Jones, 1915

330 Anonymous England c1770
Movement only. No dial.
Probably conversion from verge.
Diamond endstone. Silver pierced
ornamentation covering the whole
back plate. On the dial sub-plate is
scratched 'Benj. Sidey'.
A Benjamin Sidey of Moorfields was a
Freeman of the Clockmakers' Company
1711. Master 1761 and 1789, and died
c1790.
Bequeathed by T. Vickery, 1946

331 Samuel Toulmin England
c1770
Movement only. White enamel dial.
Gold beetle hands. Centre seconds,
beating dead seconds, above the other
hands.
Cylinder with rack giving pirouette
action; balance-spring on cylinder arbor.
The cock carries the cylinder, balance and
escape-wheel arbors. The escape-wheel
pinion passes through the hollow central
pinion and is pivoted in a bush, carrying
the seconds hand at the other end.
Diamond endstone. Signed 'Saml.
Toulmin Strand London 3361'.
Diam 38mm
See also page 41
Presented by B.L. Vulliamy, 1830

332 John Arnold England c1770
Movement only. White enamel dial.
Diamond endstone. Dust-cap.
Signed 'Jno. Arnold London No 215'.
Arnold was born 1736, a Freeman of the
Clockmakers' Company 1783, died 1799.
Diam 41mm

333 Robert Ward England c1775
Movement only. White enamel dial
signed 'Robert Ward, Abchurch Lane.
London'. Minute hand missing.
The cock is engraved and pierced with
animals with a man's head in an oval
plaque. Signed 'Robᵗ Ward. Abchurch
Lane London 5783'.
Diam 45mm
Bequeathed by T. Vickery, 1946

334 Francis Perigal England c1775
Movement only. White enamel dial.
Gold beetle hands.
Diamond endstone. Dust-cap.
Signed 'Fras. Perigal Royal Exchange
London 17912'.
Diam 33mm
Presented by Samuel E. Atkins, 1875

335 Josiah Emery England c1775
Movement only. Later dial and hands.
Ruby cylinder. Brass balance with screws.
'Sugar-tongs' bi-metallic compensation
curb. Signed 'Josiah Emery Charing Cross
London 983'.
Emery was a Freeman of the Clockmakers'
Company 1781, died 1797.
See also page 42
Nelthropp Collection

335a

325a

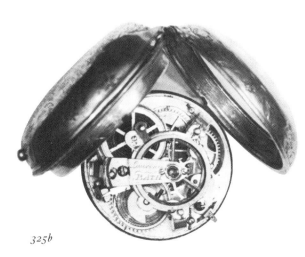

325b

335b

336 Grignion & Son England c1775
Movement only, repeating.
Diamond endstone. Silver dust-cap.
Signed 'Grignion & Son Covent Garden
London 1880'.
Diam 37mm

337 Mudge & Dutton England
HM 1779–80
Gold pair-case, outer missing. White
enamel dial. Gold hands, hour hand not
original.
Ruby endstone. Dust-cap. Signed 'Thos.
Mudge W. Dutton London 1181'.
William Dutton was a Freeman of the
Clockmakers' Company 1746.
Diam 41mm
Presented by Charles E. Atkins, 1899

338 James Tregent England c1780
Gilt pair-case. Outer covered shagreen.
White enamel dial with script signature.
Steel beetle hands.
Steel escape-wheel. Ruby endstone.
Dumb repeater. Dust-cap. Signed 'Jas.
Tregent Leicester Square London 825'.
Diams 48 and 41mm
Nelthropp Collection

339 John Decka England c1780
Gilt pair-case. Outer repoussé. White
enamel dial. Continental hands.
Signed on movement and dust-cap 'Jnọ.
Decka. London 312'.
Needlework pad in outer case.
Diams 49 and 42mm
Collinson Collection

340 Gautrin France c1780
Multi-coloured gold case.
Dials front and back, white enamel,
painted, and signed on back 'Coteau 1780'.
The time dial has an inner ring for day of
week and an outer ring for day of month.
The other dial has age and phase of moon,
Zodiac, and indicates sunrise and sunset.
Diamond-studded hands
Steel cylinder. Brass escape-wheel.
Plain brass balance. Repeating clock-
watch. There are two mainsprings, both
signed 'Vincent Juin 1811'.
The back plate is signed 'Gautrin à Paris
Nº 481' and a band round the movement is
signed 'Gautrin invenitque fecit'. The
watch has a short chain and two keys and is
contained in a Desoutter box together with
some mechanical instructions by
Desoutter.
Diam 43mm
See also page 43
Presented by G.S. Sanders

341 W. Dutton & Sons England
c1780
Movement only. Dial probably later.
Sapphire endstone. Signed 'W. Dutton &
Sons, London 1470'.
Diam 46mm
Bequeathed by T. Vickery, 1946

342 John Holmes England c1780
Movement only. White enamel dial.
Ruby endstone. Signed dust cap.
Signed 'Jnọ. Holmes Strand. London
6506', and also on dust-cap.
Diam 45mm
Nelthropp Collection

343 Alexander Cumming England
c1780
Movement only. Enamel dial.
Signed 'Alexʳ Cumming London 704' and
also on dust-cap.
Diam 36mm
Presented by Miss M. Cowles, 1960

344 James Young Scotland 1781
Movement only. White enamel dial with
subsidiary seconds dial. Gilt spade hands.
The escape-wheel has flat hook-shaped
teeth in the plane of the wheel.
Signed 'Jam. Young Perth No 103'.
The donor apparently saw the case which
was hallmarked 1781.
Diam 38mm
Nelthropp Collection

345 Ellicott England HM 1781
Silver pair-case, both hallmarked.
Stamped TC. Enamel dial. Centre seconds.
All hands gilt.
Movement and dust-cap signed 'Ellicott
London 8235'.
Diams 51 and 44mm
Collinson Collection

346 Eardley Norton England 1781
Movement only. White enamel dial.
Gold beetle hands.
Diamond endstone. Dust-cap.
Signed 'Eardley Norton London No.
7265'.
Norton was a Freeman of the Clockmakers'
Company 1770.
The donor apparently saw the case which
was hallmarked 1781.
Diam 41mm
Nelthropp Collection

347 A-L. Breguet France 1783
Gold engine-turned case with reeded

band. On back is initial 'N' surmounted by
a crown.
White enamel dial with secret signature.
Both case and dial are certainly later
replacements by Breguet.
Steel cylinder of conventional type.
No compensation. Quarter repeater.
Self winding. Signed 'Breguet a Paris $8\frac{10}{83}$'.
Breguet certificate number 2986 is of little
help as to the history of the watch, only
stating that it was bought back from a
M. Decani. However, it is said to have
been sold originally to the Grand Duke
Nicholas of Russia, later Czar Nicholas I,
who presumably had it re-cased with a
short pendant by Breguet c1800. It is
probably the oldest surviving
'perpetuelle' or self-winding watch.
See also: Chapuis & Jacquet, *La Montre
Automatique Ancienne* (1952), p.118;
Clutton & Daniels, *Watches* (1965), p.46;
Sotheby Catalogue April 20th 1968,
Lot 40.
See also page 42
Diam 52mm

347a

347b

348a

348b

348c

348 A-L. Breguet France 1784/5
Plain gold case. Long pendant. Poinçon
for 1784. White enamel dial and gold
beetle hands, probably of later date.
Plain steel cylinder. No compensation.
The dust-cap can only be removed after the
movement has been taken out of the case,
which entails removing the dial and hands.
Minute repeater of type similar to that
used by Arnold.
Signed 'Breguet A Paris No. 128$\frac{5}{85}$'.
See also: Clutton & Daniels, *Watches*
(1965), fig 305.
This watch appeared in the earlier
catalogue as a forgery but subsequent
knowledge of Breguet's work shows it to be
a very early genuine example of his work.
Diam 48mm
See also page 42

349 Marie & Campara England
HM 1786
Gold pair-case both hallmarked.
Stamped J(?)W. Enamel dial. Skeleton
fusee movement. Signed 'Marie &
Campara. London 214'.
These makers are not recorded in Britten
or Baillie.
Diams 50 and 41mm
Collinson Collection

350 Josiah Emery England c1790
Movement only. White enamel dial. Gold
arrow hands. Ruby cylinder.
Ruby endstone. Tapered helical spring.
Brass balance with four screws.

Compensation curb of two bi-metallic
strips mounted on a movable regulating
sector. Repeating. Signed 'Josiah Emery
Charing Cross London 1123'.
The movement is illustrated in Clutton &
Daniels *Watches*, (1965), fig 308.
Diam 44mm
See also page 42
Presented by Messrs Charles Frodsham,
1875

351 James Evans England HM 1790
Pair-case. Outer gilt metal. Inner silver-
gilt, hallmarked. Stamped JC. Enamel dial
signed 'Higgs & Evans London'. Gold
hands. Centre seconds. Signed on
movement and dust-cap 'Ja.ª Evans
London 9439'.
James Evans was in association with Higgs
c1785. The watch may therefore have been
re-dialled by the firm.
Diams 54 and 46mm
Collinson Collection

352 Alexander Dickie Scotland
c1790
Movement only. Enamel dial. Gold hands.
Signed 'Alex.ʳ Dickie Edinburgh 309'.
Diam 42mm
Nelthropp Collection

353 Arnold England c1790
Movement only. No dial. Centre seconds.
Signed 'Arnold London No 2865'.
This is an unidentified Arnold, not John

Arnold.
Bequeathed by T. Vickery, 1946

354 Ellicott England c1790
Movement only.
Repeater.
Signed on movement and dust-cap
'Ellicott London 8248'.
Diam 33mm

355 Jean Antoine Lepine France
Late 18th century
Movement only. No dial.
Dumb quarter repeater with one hammer.
This is a typical Lepine design with the
components supported by separate cocks
screwed to a single plate. In this watch the
centre and third wheels have Lepine's
'wolf's teeth'.
Signed 'Lepine Hger. du Roy No. 5605 a
Paris'.
Diam 50mm

356 Anonymous Late 18th century
Movement only. White enamel dial.
Minute hand missing.
Although very small the movement has a
fusee.
Diam 14mm. Thickness 6·5mm

357 Francis Perigal England
Late 18th century
Movement only. Signed 'Fras. Perigal
London 16754'.
Diam 35mm
Presented by Evan Roberts, 1904

47

358 John Brockbank England
Late 18th century
Movement only. White enamel dial. Gold
beetle hands. Centre seconds hand
between hour and minute hands.
Dust-cap.
Signed 'Brockbank London 1617'.
Diam 41mm
Presented by Samuel E. Atkins, 1875

359 John Brockbank England
Late 18th century
Movement only. White enamel dial with
no minute figures. Subsidiary seconds
dial. Gold spade hands. Dust-cap.
Signed 'Brockbank London 1824'.
Diam 50mm
Presented by Samuel E. Atkins, 1893

360 Brockbanks England
Late 18th century
Movement only. White enamel dial. Gold
beetle hands.
Dust-cap. Signed 'Brockbanks London
2796'. This signature denotes a
partnership of John and Myles Brockbank.
John was a Freeman of the Clockmakers'
Company in 1769 and Myles in 1776.
Diam 35mm
Presented by Evan Roberts, 1904

361 Alexander Cumming England
Late 18th century
Movement only. White enamel dial. Gold
spade hands. Signed 'Alexr. Cumming
London 1312'.
Cumming was a Freeman of the
Clockmakers' Company in 1781.
Diam 48mm
Presented by Evan Roberts, 1904

362 William Ross Ireland
End 18th century
Silver pair-case. White enamel dial. Gold
beetle hands.
Ruby endstone. Dust-cap.
Signed 'Wm Ross Cork. No. 383'.
Diams 56 and 48mm
Presented by John W. Carter, 1903

363 Fr Bük Austria
Early 19th century
Gilt case. Oval loop pendant. White
enamel dial. Steel looped hands. Self-
winding. Signed 'Fr Bük Bregenz'.
Diam 53mm
Nelthropp Collection

364 Milleret & Tissot Switzerland
Early 19th century
Gold case, engine-turned and enamelled
translucent green with painted rose and
pattern. The edge, bezel and pendant ring
enamelled red and white. Silver dial. Gold
looped hands.
Eight-day movement. The spring barrel is
of normal size but there is an extra wheel
in the train. Brass balance.
Signed 'Milleret & Tissot. Genève'.
Attached is a chain with links enamelled
green, and a gold seal key and case.
Diam 18mm
See also page 43
Nelthropp Collection
See also colour plate II

365 Anonymous Early 19th century
Silver engine-turned case. White enamel
dial. Small eccentric hour dial. Centre
seconds beating seconds. Cylinder with
rack giving pirouette action. Balance-
spring on cylinder arbor.
Diam 59mm

366 James McCabe England c1800
Engine-turned silver case, not original,
hallmarked 1835–6. White enamel dial.
Centre seconds hand above minute hand.
Steel spade hands.
Ruby endstone. Musical train with pinned
barrel of four tunes, five hammers striking
on four bells.
Signed 'McCabe No.460 London'.
Diam 58mm
See also page 43
Nelthropp Collection

367 Berthoud France c1800
Silver case. White enamel dial. Minutes
divided into quarters.
Centre seconds hand between hour and
minute hands. Gold beetle hands.
Regulator square above XII.
Brass balance. Going barrel with teeth at
centre of depth. Self-winding.
Signed 'Berthoud A Paris'. Also signed on
the winding weight.
Diam 57mm
See also page 43

368 A-L. Breguet France c1800
Gold case. White enamel '*souscription*'
dial and hour hand only.
Winds through the boss of the hand.
Signed 'Breguet' and also with secret
signature.
Ruby cylinder of Breguet's special type.
Compensation curb. Brass balance.
Signed 'Breguet No 518'.
A very early example of Breguet's
'*montre à souscription*'.
Diam 60mm
See also page 42
Presented by Miss V.L. Blackman, 1955

369 Brockbanks England
HM 1803–4
Silver hunter case. Oval loop pendant.
White enamel dial. Gold spade hands.
Dial winding. Dust-cap.
Signed 'Brockbanks London No 4749'.
Diam 53mm
Bequeathed by S.E. Atkins, 1898

368a

368b

370 **George Yonge** England
HM 1805–6
Gold pair-case. Inner case with chiselled
edge.
White enamel dial with subsidiary
seconds dial. Alarm hand with small circle
of figures. Gold spade hands.
Diamond endstone. Gold balance. Alarm
on bell. Signed 'Geo. Yonge Strand
London 6155'.
Diams 61 and 53mm
Nelthropp Collection

371 **A-L. Breguet** France c1805
Gold case. Stamped 442 and B1411.
White enamel '*souscription*' dial and hour
hand only. Winds through the boss of the
hand. Signed 'Breguet'.
Ruby cylinder of Breguet's special type.
Compensation curb. Brass balance.
Parachute. Signed 'Breguet No 1411'.
Unusually, there is no secret signature on
the dial which has more than the ordinary
number of divisions.
Diam 60mm
See also page 42
Collinson Collection

372 **A-L. Breguet** France c1806
Movement only, fitted in a circular brass
box.
White enamel '*souscription*' dial. Hour
hand only. Winds through boss of hand.
Signed 'Breguet et Fils' and secret
signature.
Ruby cylinder of Breguet's special type.
Compensation curb. Brass balance.
Parachute. Signed 'Breguet No.1603'.
Diam 64mm
The watch was sold in 1806 to M. Menard
for 840 francs.

373 **Jacob Jackson** England c1815
Movement only. Sapphire cylinder. Gold
balance. Jewelled movement.
Signed 'Jacob Jackson Quay Bristol
No. 4793'.
Bequeathed by T. Vickery, 1946
Diam 43mm

374 **John Roger Arnold** England
HM 1816–17
Gold case. White enamel dial signed
'Arnold 1816'. Gold spade hands.
Steel balance. 'Sugar-tongs'
compensation curb mounted on
regulator sector.
Signed 'Jno. R. Arnold London
No. 3728'.
Diam 51mm

375 **Du Bois & Fils** France c1820
Gold case signed on cuvette 'Dubois et
fils'. Enamel dial signed 'Dubois et fils'.
Steel moon hands.
Repeating movement. The watch is as new
and probably unfinished as it was
intended to have a musical train, but this
was never put in and the cavity to receive it
is covered with a gilt plate. But the
cuvette is engraved with musical emblems
and has a winding-hole. There are two
slides on the band, both inoperative.
One was intended for the repeater and one
for the music.
Diam 55mm
Collinson Collection

376 **John Roger Arnold** England
c1820
Movement only. White enamel dial
signed 'Arnold 207'.
Gold spade hands (hour broken).
Ruby cylinder. Steel balance.
Compensation curb. Going barrel.
Prest's keyless winding. Signed 'Jn. R.
Arnold London Patent no 207'.
Arnold was a Freeman of the
Clockmakers' Company 1796, Master
1817, died 1843. His foreman Thomas
Prest patented a keyless winding device in
1820 which was used by Arnold, mostly on
ruby cylinder watches.
Diam 49mm
Nelthropp Collection

377 **Feodor Kovalaski** Probably
Switzerland c1820
Silver case stamped 1–568 and 14569.
Enamel dial with gold calendar hand and
circle.
Continental bridge and coqueret.
Regulator engraved '*Avance*' and
'*Retard*'. Fusee. Signed 'Feodor
Kovalaski. Ekatemoslav' (now
Kirovgrad).
Despite the Russian signature the style of
the movement is clearly Continental,
almost certainly Swiss.
Diam 70mm

378 **John Roger Arnold** England
HM 1821–2
Gold case. Silver dial with subsidiary
seconds dial. Steel hands.
Stem winding without back ratchet.
Hand setting is by key and square.
Ruby cylinder. Steel balance with a
broad rim. 'Sugar-tongs' compensation
curb carrying one curb-pin fixed to the
regulator arm. Signed 'Jno. R. Arnold
London. Patent. No. 47'.
This early system of keyless winding was
invented by Arnold's foreman Thomas
Prest in 1820.

371

378a

378b

Diam 53mm
See also page 43
Presented by Executors of W.T. Berners,
1930

379 John Roger Arnold England
HM 1823
Silver case stamped 19 and TH. Enamel
dial signed 'Arnold No 91'.
Subsidiary seconds dial. Hands not
original.
Ruby cylinder. Steel balance with broad
rim. Stem winding without back ratchet.
Hand setting by key and square.
Signed 'Jno. R. Arnold London No 91.
Patent'.
This early system of keyless winding was
invented by Arnold's foreman, Thomas
Prest, in 1820.
Diam 53mm

380 Carpenter England HM 1826
Silver engine-turned case. Stamped WH.
Enamel dial. Subsidiary seconds dial.
Gold hands.
Ruby cylinder. Brass balance with poising
weights. Partly-jewelled train.
Signed 'Carpenter London No.1112'.
Diam 48mm
Nelthropp Collection

381 Ingold France c1830
Gold engine-turned case. Stamped 271.
Knob pendant. Silver engine-turned dial.
Plain balance and compensation curb.
Quarter repeater employing Breguet's
'pull-out' plunger in the pendant.
Signed on dome 'Ingold. Elève de
Breguet, Palais Royal No. 638', also
'No 177'.
Diam 51mm
Collinson Collection

382 Czapek & Cie Switzerland c1840
Gold case, black enamelled with portrait
in grisaille. White enamel dial.
Signed 'Czapek et Cie Geneve No 2522'.
Diam 18mm
Presented by Smiths Industries Ltd, 1968

383 Grohé England c1840
Gold engine-turned case of foreign style.
Enamel dial.
Repeater and alarm. Signed 'Grohé.
Wigmore Street. Cavendish Square,
converted'. Grohé succeeded Hayley &
Son at 7 Wigmore Street in 1834 and was
succeeded, c1842, by John Pennington.
Diam 57mm
Collinson Collection.

384 Thomas Earnshaw England
c1840
Movement only. No dial. Dial plate has
7812 stamped on it.
Half-plate movement with two cocks.
Plain brass balance. Signed 'Tho.ˢ
Earnshaw. High Holborn London'.
Diam 38mm
Presented by Evan Roberts, 1913

385 Dwerrihouse Ogston & Bell
England c1850
Movement only. Silver engine-turned dial
with matt centre. Subsidiary seconds dial.
Pump-winding. Going barrel. Multi-cock
movement. Signed (on 3 cocks)
'Dwerrihouse Ogston & Bell No 13165'.
They commenced in partnership at
131 Mount Street, c1840.
Diam 35mm
Presented by Evan Roberts, 1913

386 Edward Darville England c1850
Movement only. Silver dial with rayed
engine turning and painted figures.
Signed 'Edw. Darville. London 5877' on
barrel cover.
The layout of the movement is similar to
watches made by Ilbery & Bovet for the
Eastern market.
Diam 46mm
Bequeathed by T. Vickery, 1946

387 Aubert Capt Switzerland c1850
Gold case. Engraved gold dial.
Signed 'Aubert Capt 8027'.
Short gold chain and key attached.
Diam 16mm

388 Anonymous Switzerland
Mid 19th century
Gold engine-turned case. Silver engine-
turned dial with aperture for flirting hour
figures. Eccentric polished ring for
minutes with steel hands. Sunk
subsidiary seconds dial.
Steel balance. Lepine calibre. Going
barrel.
Diam 45mm
Nelthropp Collection

389 Anonymous Switzerland c1880
Gold case. Movement swings out. Very
thin. Stamped IF MD 1426.
Enamel dial.
The fusee movement is totally enclosed.
Diam 57mm
See also page 43
Presented by Sidney Sanders, 1930

390 Anonymous Probably Switzerland
c1900
Movement only. Included is pedometer
mechanism. Enamel dial with small
subsidiary dials for seconds, quarter miles
and miles up to 50.
See also page 43
Collinson Collection

391 A. S. & F. Switzerland c1900
Metal case with gilt bezel and keyless
winding. 'Mystery watch' with
transparent dial with no apparent motion
work. Signed 'A.S. & F. Mysterieuse.
Breveté SGDG'.
See Plate 120 of Jaquet & Chapuis,
The Swiss Watch (1953)
Diam 54mm
See also page 43
Collinson Collection

Watches with duplex escapement

The duplex escapement is only moderately represented in the Collection, but this is not a serious disadvantage, since it appeared in about 1782 fully developed, and never altered significantly in its life-span of a little over a century. During the eighteenth century several experiments were made with clock and watch escapements where one set of teeth was concerned with locking and unlocking and the other with impulse. However, in the form in which it became popular it was a British innovation. In 1782 Thomas Tyrer took out a patent in which he described an 'horizontal escapement for a watch to act with two wheels'; but by about 1790 the London makers had developed a single escape-wheel with two rows of teeth on it. A set of long pointed teeth were responsible for locking on a sapphire roller set in the balance-staff, while a set of teeth rising vertically from the plane of the escape-wheel gave impulse to a long impulse pallet. It was an extremely delicate thing to make and it is hard to see what advantage over the two separate wheels it was supposed to possess. Certainly the Continental makers, notably Breguet and Jurgensen, continued to employ two separate, co-axial wheels.

From about 1810 to 1850 the duplex escapement virtually held the field for high-grade British pocket watches where precision was not the sole criterion, and even so, it was capable of performing very creditably. From before 1800 it is rarely found and the Collection is fortunate in possessing about half a dozen exhibits from this early period including one of the double-wheel variety (catalogue number 633).

In many old watches a cylinder escapement has been replaced by duplex and it is very difficult to detect when this has happened, since it could be done with no alteration to the layout. However, catalogue number 392 has every appearance of being in its original condition, and if so it is a very early (if not the earliest surviving) example of the duplex escapement in a watch. It is in a very large watch, with separate hour-striking and repeating trains, by the important precision maker John Grant and is hallmarked 1789. It is curious that such a complicated watch should have been intended for the Turkish market, but its dial with Turkish numerals appears to be original. The watch (serial number 1638) is also one of the earliest surviving examples of Grant's work, which is discussed at greater length in the introduction to the section on the lever escapement.

Among early makers employing the duplex escapement, none made finer or more imposing watches than the Vulliamys and catalogue number 396 is a movement, probably by Benjamin Vulliamy, which is in mint condition and seems never to have been used or cased. The Vulliamy three-letter numbering code has never been deciphered. By the end of the nineteenth century when the duplex escapement was surviving only as an archaism (it was still being made into the twentieth century and catalogue number 417 is an example) it was revived in the cheap American Waterbury watch, but unfortunately the Collection does not possess an example.

The duplex escapement is really a combination of the cylinder and chronometer escapements, since it uses the frictional rest system of locking (but on a much smaller radius than the cylinder) coupled with the chronometer method of giving impulse. Its main disadvantage is that it can accept only very little wear in the points of the locking teeth or in the balance-staff pivots.

Duplex escapement

392 Grant England HM 1789
Silver pair-case, both hallmarked.
Dust-cap signed as on movement.
Enamel dial. Turkish figures. Signed
'Grant. London'. Steel beetle hands.
Clock watch and separate quarter-
repeating train. The earliest duplex in the
Collection.
Signed 'Grant Fleet Street no 1638'.
Diams 75 and 65mm
See also page 51
Collinson Collection

393 Thomas Wright England c1790
Silver-gilt case. White enamel dial.
Gold hands. Going barrel. Brass balance.
Compensation curb added later. Signed
'Wright Watchmaker to the King
Poultry 7714'.
Wright took out the patent for Earnshaw's
spring-detent escapement. Earnshaw may
have made this very (for the date) thin
watch.
Diam 35mm
Presented by A. & J. Smith, Dublin, 1934

394 Mudge & Dutton England
HM 1791–2
Gold pair-case. Stirrup pendant. White
enamel dial. Gold beetle hands.
Half-quarter dumb repeater. Dust-cap.
Signed 'Tho. Mudge W. Dutton
London 1432'.
Diams 53 and 45mm
Presented by Charles Frodsham, 1869

395 Anonymous Continental c1800
Movement only. White enamel dial.
Subsidiary dials of equal size for hours,
minutes and seconds. Gold arrow hands.
Pierced plate with design of intertwined
serpents acting as top plate, arranged
symmetrically about the spring barrel
which has no cock. The balance-cock is on
the same level as the plate.
Oval shape, length 57mm
Presented by F.B. Adams & Sons, 1849

396 Vulliamy England c1800
Movement only. Typical Vulliamy hands
with skeleton heart-shaped ends. Quarter
repeater. Compensation curb.
Signed 'Vulliamy London rxu'.
This is probably by Benjamin, son of
Justin Vulliamy. The Vulliamy numbering
code has not been deciphered. The
Vulliamys were early exponents of the
duplex escapement. This example is
unusual in having a bridge-type balance-
cock. It seems doubtful if this movement
was ever used or cased.

Diam 50mm
See also *Antiquarian Horology*, March
1954, p 15, and March 1956, p 142.
See page 51

397 Sigismund Rentsch England
Early 19th century
Movement only. White enamel dial.
Subsidiary seconds dial. Gold spade hands.
Steel balance with rating screws. Spiral
bi-metallic compensation curb. Signed
'Rentsch. Queen Street Golden Square
London'.
See *Antiquarian Horology*, December
1966, pp 164–9.
Diam 46mm
Nelthropp Collection

398 John Barwise England
HM 1808–9
Gold case engine-turned. White enamel
dial with subsidiary seconds dial. Dust-cap.
Brass balance. Diamond endstone. Dumb
repeater by turning and then pushing a rod
running through the pendant.
Signed 'Barwise London 4278'.
Diam 54mm
Nelthropp Collection

399 John Gibson England
HM 1808–9
Gold case. White enamel dial with
subsidiary seconds dial. Gold spade hands.
Dust-cap. Two-armed bi-metallic balance.
Signed 'Jn. Gibson London 1533'.
Diam 56mm
Nelthropp Collection

400 Barrauds England c1814
Movement only. White enamel dial.
Subsidiary seconds dial. Signed
'8368 Barrauds London'. Hands missing.
The dial plate is stamped 1810. Plain brass
balance. Undecorated cock. Signed
'Barrauds Cornhill London 8368'.
See C. Jagger, *P.P. Barraud*, p 143.
Diam 40mm
Bequeathed by Miss E.M. Barraud, 1972

401 Anonymous England
HM 1818–19
Gold case. Gold dial with subsidiary
seconds dial. Steel spade hands.
Although the external appearance of the
watch is all consistent with the date of the
hallmark the movement was replaced
entirely in the second half of the
nineteenth century. It has polished,
spotted plates, bi-metallic compensation
balance, helical spring, gold escape-wheel,
and fusee.

Gold chain and key attached.
Diam 50mm
Presented by Sir David Salomons Bt, 1924

402 Johnson England c1820
Movement only. Enamel dial. No seconds
dial.
Bi-metallic compensation balance. The
regulator index is on the table of the cock
which also has a mask engraved on it.
Signed 'Johnson. London. 1849'.
This maker is not recorded.
Diam 48mm
Nelthropp Collection

403 Thomas Earnshaw England
c1820
Movement only.
Flat steel balance. Dial plate stamped
1810. Signed 'Tho: Earnshaw London
No. 4471'.
Bequeathed by T. Vickery, 1946

404 Richard Webster England
c1820
Movement only. Enamel dial signed
'Webster 3384'. Subsidiary seconds dial.
Gold spade hands.
Bi-metallic compension curb. Plain brass
balance. Signed 'R.d Webster. Change
Alley London no 3384'.
This must be Richard Webster who took
over from his father, Richard, in 1802,
at the age of 17. See *Antiquarian Horology*,
September 1955, p 109.
Diam 46mm
Presented by A. & J. Smith, Dublin, 1934

405 William Hardy England c1820
Gold case. Hallmark illegible. White
enamel dial with HAROLD LOVELL in lieu of
hour figures. Subsidiary seconds dial.
Steel spade hands.
Bi-metallic compensation balance.
Dust-cap. Fusee.
Signed 'Will.m Hardy London 721'.
Diam 53mm
Presented by Sidney Sanders, 1932

406 James McCabe England
HM 1822
Gold hunter case. White enamel dial.
Subsidiary seconds dial. Gold spade hands.
Ring pendant.
Later bi-metallic compensation balance.
Diamond endstone. Repeater.
Signed 'Jas. McCabe Royal Exchange
London 10781'.
Diam 53mm
Presented by W.N. Vokes, 1932

407 R. Wright England HM 1824
Gold case. Engine-turned back. Stamped
HG 3063. Gold dial, centre engine turned.
Subsidiary seconds dial. Fleur-de-lys
hands. Compensation balance.
Signed 'R. Wright 3063 – 1841'.
Collinson Collection

408 Grimaldi & Johnson England
c1825
Movement only. Enamel dial signed and
numbered 431. Spoon-shaped hour hand.
Repeater on gongs of rectangular section.
Compensation curb. Signed 'Grimaldi &
Johnson. Strand. London No 5618'.
Grimaldi & Johnson traded at number
431 Strand and it is to this that the number
on the dial refers.
Diam 48mm
Bequeathed by T. Vickery, 1946

409 Edward Baker England
HM 1827–8
Gold case. White enamel with subsidiary
seconds dial. Gold loop hands.
Bi-metallic compensation balance.
Signed 'Edwd. Baker 33 White Lion St.
London No. 998'.
Diam 50mm
Bequeathed by Sir Jamsetjee
Jejeebhoy Bt, 1898

410 James Arnold England
HM 1829
Silver case. Enamel dial. Subsidiary
seconds dial.
Plain steel balance.
Signed 'Ja.s Arnold London No 994'.
Diam 53mm
Collinson Collection

411 John Carter England
Mid 19th century
Movement only. White enamel dial.
Subsidiary seconds dial. Gold hands.
Bi-metallic compensation balance. Signed
'John Carter Cornhill London No. 3218'.
Diam 38mm
Presented by Evan Roberts, 1912

412 Shrapnell & Son England and
Switzerland HM 1850
Silver engine-turned case. Stamped J.H.
Enamel dial, inscribed 'Duplex' round
boss of hands.
Skeleton movement, all elaborately
engraved, of Swiss origin. Going barrel.
The only signature is on the dome
'Shrapnell & Son London'.
Diam 51mm
Collinson Collection

413 Justin Vulliamy England
HM 1852 (recased)
Silver case with modern type of pendant.
Later white enamel dial with minute
figures. Steel spade hands.
Signed 'Justin Vulliamy London xna'.
Diam 47mm
Nelthropp Collection

414 Anonymous Switzerland c1860
Gilt-metal case. Double dial, both giving
time but one has subsidiary and the other
centre seconds (the reason is not obvious).
Chinese duplex. The regulator is in the
bezel. Also in the bezel is a slide which,
when moved, exposes a toothed wheel
which sets the hands on both dials.
(To expose the mechanism it is necessary
to remove two pins in the bezel of the
winding-side dial.)
There is no signature but the hands with
long ends are typical of Fleurier. The
watch is difficult to date but 1860 seems
reasonable.
Diam 56mm
Collinson Collection

415 Anonymous Switzerland c1870
Silver case. Glazed back. Enamel dial.
Centre seconds. Chinese duplex
escapement with Jacot balance.
Movement with curved bridges.
Probably by a Fleurier maker but as the
regulator dial is engraved S & F the watch
may be of the Ilbery type.
See A. Chapuis, *La Montre Chinoise*,
pp 162, 169.
Diam 58mm

416 Massey & Windham England
HM 1883–4
Gold case. Gold engraved dial with
subsidiary seconds dial. Steel spade hands.
Bi-metallic compensation balance.
Dust-cap. Signed 'Massey & Windham,
4, Birchin Lane & 78, Cornhill. London'.
Diam 50mm
Presented by Ralph Hall, 1935

417 New England Watch Company
America c1910
Nickel case. Skeleton dial.
Skeleton movement, glazed on both covers.
Signed 'N.E.W.CO'.
Diam 50mm
See also page 51
Bequeathed by M.L. Bateman, 1966

Watches with detent escapement

Various people experimented with free escapements in which impulse to the balance was imparted by the escape-wheel and the train was locked by a detent. Indeed, Galileo's pendulum escapement, catalogue number 629, pre dating Huygens, conforms exactly to this description, and by 1740 Thiout, at any rate on paper, had applied roughly the same arrangement to a watch. The defect of both was that since they lacked a passing spring the unlocking and impulse had to take place at the end of the pendulum or balance arc, at the furthest possible point from the theoretically correct neutral point, or line of centres. Pierre Le Roy overcame this defect in various more or less complicated escapements between 1750 and 1765, but it had to wait for the genius of John Arnold to produce the beautifully simple solution of the passing-spring in 1772. From that point stem all subsequent developments of the detent escapement. For the next ten years Arnold developed his escapement in pocket and marine timekeepers: the former to a point where they would keep time over very long periods within an error of four seconds a day at worst, and the latter at a price which made them attainable by sea captains in charge of any important vessel. Over this decade there was no one else in the field and it was only from about 1782 that competitors began to enter. It may therefore be said without question that John Arnold developed the precision watch and made the public aware of its practical importance. At the same time, the sturdy elegance and high finish of his products made their ownership more than a mere matter of utility and it is fortunate that they are quite well represented in the Collection.

Until 1782 Arnold's detents were all pivoted but from that year he mounted them on a spring. His younger and jealous competitor, Earnshaw, said he was forced to do this because his pivoted detents tended to operate sluggishly and allow the escapement to run through. This may perhaps have been true, with the inferior oils then available, but it is certainly not a defect from which Arnold's pivoted detent watches suffer in present-day wear. When Arnold mounted his detent on a spring he revised his whole escapement in a not entirely satisfactory way so that the spring could be in tension. The more empirical Earnshaw merely took Arnold's pivoted detent and mounted it on a spring in compression, which worked perfectly well and eventually drove Arnold's version from the field, although the latter remained in use for over thirty years. Several of the Arnolds in the Collection have been converted to Earnshaw's escapement but even so, many more unconverted Arnold than Earnshaw watches have survived and are represented in the Collection.

Earnshaw detent watches before 1800 are markedly rare and the Collection is fortunate in possessing in catalogue number 427 (illustrated) one of his finest and earliest surviving watches, in a silver pair-case hallmarked for 1791. The typical Earnshaw compensation balance has the large wedge-shaped weights which placed such a dangerous load on the pivots; and the balance-spring – always Earnshaw's weakest point – is a plain spiral. In this watch the movement is hinged to the case but later, he applied no decoration to the movement and screwed it into the case.

John Arnold frequently had his watches brought back to him to incorporate his latest improvements, especially balance-wheels, and many pivoted detents were replaced by his spring detents. Unaltered early Arnold watches are, therefore, very rare and in catalogue number 419 (illustrated), his number 28 contains his earliest surviving pivoted detent (apart from an early experimental layout owned by the Royal Society). The silver-gilt case is hallmarked for 1776 but the 's'[1] balance was the first to be made in any quantity and was current from 1779–82.

419a

419b

[1] The description of Arnold balances as s, oz, yz and z has been coined by Dr V. Mercer in his book *John Arnold & Son* and is now generally adopted. The letters are roughly descriptive of the arrangement of the arms and rims of the balances.

Unlike Earnshaw, Arnold was always concerned to achieve as light a balance as possible for his pocket watches. This pattern has a very light steel wheel to which are fixed two 's' shaped bi-metallic strips with a short rod and weight fixed to each. These move in and out under changes of temperature, thus compensating for the changes in elasticity of the balance-spring.

Next came the 'oz' balance which was current from 1782 and came in with the spring detent. The 'o' is a plain steel wheel and the 'z' is two bi-metallic strips fixed to the steel wheel and curved in shape parallel to the rim of the wheel. The final 'z' balance dispensed with the 'o' consisting of two arms (the diagonal line of the z) and two curved bi-metallic strips (the top and bottom strokes of the z, but curved). Marine chronometers usually had a 'YZ' which had three radiating arms and three curved bi-metallic strips.

By far the greatest number of surviving John Arnold watches are from 1782 onwards (he died in 1799) and for these a new system of numbering was introduced, in the form of a fraction in which the upper figure is 301 less than the lower. Prior to this Arnold's system of numbering, partly fractional, was distinctly complex and may be studied in Dr Vaudrey Mercer's book *John Arnold & Son*. The 'oz' balance is well represented, the oldest, catalogue number 421, being a movement dating from about 1787; but there is a complete gold watch, catalogue number 424 (Arnold$\frac{292}{593}$) hallmarked for 1788. Catalogue number 432 (Arnold$\frac{513}{814}$) hallmarked 1796 has a z balance. All the last three are signed 'John Arnold & Son', after he had taken his son John Roger into partnership.

422a

Catalogue number 422 (illustrated) is a unique silver watch by Larcum Kendall. It was Kendall who was employed to build a replica of Harrison's H4 and he later built two further watches incorporating variations of the Harrison theme, but still basically verges. Catalogue number 422, hallmarked for 1786, has a curious type of pivoted detent and as far as is known was Kendall's only attempt at this escapement or at a precision pocket watch. Its superb finish and highly elegant regulator dial make it one of the most handsome watches of its decade; yet with its curious escapement and spiral compensation curb it is archaic compared with anything Arnold had done during the previous decade.

Two firms early in the pocket chronometer field were Brockbanks and Barwise; both remarkable for the elegance of their watches and dials. Both are well represented, of which catalogue number 433 by Barwise is illustrated and is an admirable example of the multiple regulator type dial.

422b

Illustrated in colour, but not at all typical of Brockbanks, is catalogue number 440. It possesses a magnificent movement containing a half-quarter repeating train on three gongs; but it is the gold case and dial, hallmarked for 1812, that are truly startling by their robust Regency ostentation – vulgarity so virile and vigorous that in fact it succeeds completely. The full-hunter case is chiselled and engraved in four-coloured gold. The gold dome has a complicated engine-turned pattern; and the gold dial has a sunk centre section, engine-turned, and covered with translucent red enamel. The serpentine hands are gold.

Detent escapements sometimes had a duplex-type escape-wheel, used in just the same way except that the pointed teeth lock on an ordinary spring detent instead of the sapphire roller of the true duplex. An example of this is catalogue number 436, by Paul Philip Barraud, dated 1800.

[2]The difference between a constant-force escapement and a remontoir is explained on page 89

Variants of the balance-spring are the plain spiral spring of catalogue number 447, a watch of 1823 by Parkinson and Frodsham, with the refinement of the balance-spring stud being on a flexible arm which aids the even coiling and uncoiling of the balance-spring. Much later in the century (1873) is catalogue number 451 with the rare duo-in-uno spring.

Breguet is represented in this section by catalogue number 448; an extremely plain watch of 1830, probably intended for use as a deck watch.

Catalogue number 449 is a watch made by Alexander Watkins for the Great Exhibition of 1851. It is also a repeater and quarter-striking clock-watch, despite which it is hopefully designed to go for eight days.

Certainly the most complicated escapement of any watch in the Collection is catalogue number 435 (illustrated) which has survived as a movement only. It is by Charles Haley, dating from about 1800, and is only questionably to be regarded as a detent escapement, since between the escape-wheel and the detent is interposed a most complicated and delicate constant force arrangement.[2] Unlocking takes place via the detent and passing spring in the usual way, but impulse is delivered by an arm mounted on a slender spiral spring. The escape-wheel then is concerned only to re-tension the spiral constant-force spring after each impulse. Like Mudge's constant-force marine timekeeper, there can be no means of compensating for variations in the elasticity of the constant-force spring under changes of temperature, and anyway the escapement is dangerously prone to tripping. Nevertheless it is of great technical interest as being one of the exceedingly few pocket watches ever made to contain a constant-force escapement.

Catalogue number 452 (illustrated) is a watch of the highest quality, hallmarked for 1879, by the Swiss firm of Girard Perregaux, comprising a pivoted detent escapement mounted on a tourbillon. The Continental makers continued mostly to favour the pivoted detent escapement and some particularly fine specimens were made by Louis Berthoud and, later, the Jurgensens. They were considered particularly appropriate for tourbillons where the whole momentum of the tourbillon carriage has to be arrested by the detent. For the same reason, when Breguet employed a spring detent on a tourbillon he employed the Peto cross-detent layout.

Detent escapement watches continued to be made in England, although but rarely, until almost the First World War in 1914, but the latest example in the Collection dates from 1883. It is interesting in having a keyless-wound fusee movement (number 453). Appropriately, it comes from the firm of Thomas Mercer who still make marine chronometers and chronometer carriage clocks and whose family has long been, and still are, closely associated with the Clockmakers' Company.

Few watches in the Collection have a greater sentimental appeal than catalogue number 429 (illustrated). It is a John Arnold & Son, $\frac{485}{786}$ which places it at about 1794, but it was substantially rebuilt in 1840 probably by John Roger Arnold, since the signature on the dial has a type of Gothic lettering frequently employed by him. At the same time it was re-cased in silver, converted to Earnshaw's type of detent (which John Roger quite often employed, as well as the Arnold type) and given a new balance typical of the period. This watch was used by a Mr Belville from about 1834 to carry the correct time from Greenwich Observatory to the trade in London. When he died in 1856 his widow carried on the service until

1892, when his daughter, Miss Ruth Belville, made the weekly journey for a small fee, which was cheerfully paid although the practical need for the service had long passed. She was a great character, always dressed in black, and carried the watch on a piece of string attached to a safety-pin or loose in her shopping bag. She always referred to the watch as 'Mr. Arnold'. She died in 1943, aged 90, having been a pensioner of the Clockmakers' Company for many years. Her executors presented her watch to the Company.

Detent escapement

418 John Arnold England
c1775 & 1808 . .
Later gold pair-case hallmarked 1812–13. White enamel dial. Gold hands (hour not original). Polished steel centre seconds hand between hour and minute hands. Plain balance with compensation curb. Stop lever. Engraved round the dust-cap is 'Compensation slide balance-spring and other corrections by Earnshaw Jan 1808'. Signed 'Jno. Arnold London 277'.
This watch is in a series by John Arnold with verge or cylinder escapement and as indicated by the engraving on the dust-cap, it was converted to detent in 1808.
See V. Mercer, *John Arnold & Son*, p 209
Diams 50 and 45mm
Presented by Percy Webster, 1925

419 John Arnold England
HM 1776–7
Silver-gilt case with monogram CM surrounded by chiselled wreaths. Oval loop pendant.
White enamel dial. Subsidiary seconds dial. Steel hands. Pivoted detent. s-shaped balance. Helical spring. Signed 'John Arnold Invt. et Fecit No.28'.
This is the earliest recorded surviving pocket watch by Arnold with his pivoted detent escapement. The s-balance is a slightly later addition, being of the type employed by Arnold from 1779–82.
See V. Mercer, *John Arnold & Son*, pp 47–50 and 209, plates 62, 63.
Diam 63mm
See also page 54
Presented by Charles Frodsham & Co, 1875
Illustrated on page 54

420 Thomas Martin England
HM 1780–1 & c1801
Gold case with invisible hinges. Stirrup pendant.

White enamel dial. Subsidiary seconds dial. Gold loop hands.
Spring detent and helical spring, not original. Two-arm bi-metallic compensation balance not original. These modifications were possibly carried out by Jamison in 1801 (see below) or even later. Signed 'Martin No.1 Royal Exchange' and 'Repaired by Geo. Jamison 1801'.
Diam 63mm
Atkins Bequest, 1898

421 John Arnold & Son England
c1787
Movement only. No dial.
Spring detent. oz balance. Original helical spring replaced by flat steel spring with overcoil. Signed 'John Arnold & Son London Inv. et Fecit $\frac{251}{552}$'.
Diam 43mm
See also page 55
Bequeathed by T. Vickery, 1946

422 Larcum Kendall England
HM 1786–7
Silver pair-case. Stirrup pendant. White enamel dial. Subsidiary dials for hours and seconds.
Pivoted detent escapement, in which the passing spring is operated by an inclined plane on the balance staff. Harrison's maintaining power. Brass balance with spiral bi-metallic compensation curb. Signed 'L. Kendall London B+y'.
Kendall was born 1721 and died 1795 and this watch was purchased at his sale for £30 by Benjamin Vulliamy and presented by B.L. Vulliamy in 1849.
See *Antiquarian Horology*, March 1961, p172. Also Clutton & Daniels, *Watches*, p 109 and figs. 35, 313–14.
Diams 63 and 55mm
See also page 55
Illustrated on page 55

423 John Antes England   HM 1787–8
Silver pair-case. Oval loop pendant. White enamel dial. Subsidiary seconds dial. Steel beetle hands.

Spring detent escapement being a crude version of Earnshaw's arrangement. Plain steel balance with a very small balance-spring. Semi-skeletonised back plate. Signed 'John Antes London'. This maker is not otherwise recorded.
Diams 71 and 61mm
Presented by Edwin W. Streeter, 1895

424 John Arnold & Son England
HM 1788–9
Gold case.
White enamel dial. Subsidiary seconds dials. Gold spade hands. Engraved '292'. Spring detent. oz balance. Gold helical balance-spring of 4 turns. Signed 'John Arnold & Son Invt. et Fect. 292/593'.
Diam 53mm
See also page 55

425 Brockbanks England
HM 1790–1
Silver pair-case. Oval loop pendant. White enamel dial. Subsidiary dials for hours and seconds. Central minute hand. Gold spade hands.
Spring detent. Helical spring. The escapement has been altered. Three-arm bi-metallic compensation balance with wedge weights.
Signed 'Brockbanks London No. 3173'. Brockbanks was a firm composed of John Brockbank, a Freeman of the Clockmakers' Company 1769, and his brother Myles, a Freeman 1776 and died 1821.
Diams 68 and 58mm
Atkins Bequest, 1898

426 Brockbanks England
HM 1791–2
Silver pair-case. White enamel dial. Subsidiary seconds dial. Gold spade hands.
Spring detent of Earnshaw's type. Helical spring. Three-arm bi-metallic compensation balance with very large weights. The escapement has been altered. Signed 'Brockbanks London No. 3499'.
Diams 63 and 57mm
Atkins Bequest, 1898

427a

427b

429a

429b

427 Thomas Earnshaw England
HM 1791–2
Silver pair-case. Oval loop pendant.
White enamel dial. Subsidiary seconds
dial. Engraved 'Thomas Earnshaw Invt et
Fecit No. 58'.
Spring detent. Two-arm bi-metallic
compensation balance with wedge weights.
Signed 'Thos. Earnshaw London Invt. et
Fecit. no 1514'.
Earnshaw's system of double numbering is
not understood.
Diams 57 and 48mm
See also page 54
Presented by Vice-Admiral Sir Lawrence
E. Power, 1921

428 John Arnold & Son England
c1794
Engine-turned silver case, not original.
White enamel dial. Subsidiary seconds
dial. Gold spade hands.
Spring detent. Helical spring. Three-arm
platinum balance, not original. (The
original balance would have been a z.)
Signed 'John Arnold & Son Invt et Fect
459/760'.
Diam 50mm
Nelthropp Collection

429 John Arnold & Son England
c1794
Silver case, not original, hallmarked 1840.
Enamel dial. Subsidiary seconds dial.
Gold spade hands.
Spring detent, later converted to
Earnshaw's arrangement, and later type of
two-arm compensation balance.
Signed 'John Arnold & Son, London.

Invenit & fecit $\frac{485}{786}$'.
Diam 55mm
This watch, always known as 'Mr Arnold',
was presented by the Executors of Miss
Ruth Belville, with whom it had a long
history.
See also page 56

430 John Arnold & Son England
HM 1794–5
Gold case. Enamel dial. Subsidiary
seconds dial. Later steel hands.
Spring detent, later converted to
Earnshaw's arrangement. Compensation
balance not original. Signed 'John Arnold
& Son London No. 138 Invt et Fec.'.
Originally had a YZ or z balance. See
V. Mercer, *John Arnold & Son*, p 210.
Presented by the Lords Commissioners of
the Admiralty, 1906

431 John Arnold England c1790
Silver case, not original, hallmarked
1838–9.
Enamel dial. Subsidiary seconds dial.
Spring detent, not original, converted to
Earnshaw's type.
Signed 'Arnold & Son London 112'.
Diam 63mm
Presented by the Lords Commissioners of
the Admiralty, 1906

432 John Arnold & Son England
HM 1796–7
Gold case. White enamel dial. Subsidiary
seconds dial. Inscribed '513'. Gold arrowhead hands.

433b

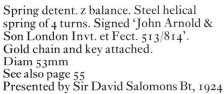

433a

435

Spring detent. z balance. Steel helical
spring of 4 turns. Signed 'John Arnold &
Son London Invt. et Fect. 513/814'.
Gold chain and key attached.
Diam 53mm
See also page 55
Presented by Sir David Salomons Bt, 1924

433 John Barwise   England
HM 1799–1800
Gold case. Stamped vw. White enamel
dial signed 'Barwise London' with
subsidiary dials for hours, minutes and
seconds. Up-and-down indicator.
Gold hands.
Spring detent, the escapement a
lightened version of Earnshaw's
arrangement. Solid three-arm brass
balance with two bi-metallic arms fixed to
it. Signed 'Barwise London 158'.
Diam 61mm
See also page 55
Presented by Sir David Salomons Bt, 1924

434 Charles Haley   England
Late 18th century
Movement only. White enamel dial.
Subsidiary seconds dial. Gold loop hands.
Pivoted detent. Balance similar in type to
Arnold's oz. Signed 'Chas. Haley London
Invt. et Fecit. CA/1513'.
Haley was a Freeman of the Clockmakers'
Company 1781.
Diam 43mm
Presented by Francis B. Adams, 1869

435 Charles Haley   London
Late 18th century
Movement only. Enamel dial with
subsidiary dials for hours and seconds.
Spring detent with constant force impulse
delivered by a spiral spring placed between
the escape-wheel and balance-staff.
Helical balance-spring. Signed 'Cs. Haley
Invt et Fecit London P/D.N.'.
Haley was a Freeman of the Clockmakers'
Company 1781.
See Clutton & Daniels, *Watches*, p 124
and fig 68.
Diam 53mm
See also page 56
Presented by Francis B. Adams, 1869

436 Paul Philip Barraud   England
HM 1800–1
Gold case. Oval section pendant.
White enamel dial. Subsidiary seconds
dial. Steel loop hands.
Spring detent. The escape-wheel has two
sets of teeth for locking and impulse.
Three-arm compensation balance.
Signed 'Barraud London. No 101'.
The escapement is attributed to Owen
Robinson and consists of using a duplex-
type escape-wheel in a chronometer.
See C. Jagger, *P.P. Barraud*, p 78 and
plate VI (a); also T. Reid, *Treatise on
Clock and Watchmaking,* plate IX, fig. 53
Diam 58mm
See also page 55
Nelthropp Collection

437 Paul Philip Barraud England
c1805
Engine-turned silver case, hallmarked
1793, but not original to this watch.
White enamel dial. Subsidiary seconds
dial.
Spring detent of Earnshaw's type.
Ruby endstone. Brass balance 'sugar-
tongs' compensation curb. Spiral spring.
Signed 'Barraud 32/5816', on dial, and
'Barraud. London' on movement.
This number does not fit into any known
series by Barraud and may have been made
for him by Earnshaw.
See C. Jagger, *P.P. Barraud*, pp 101–2 and
plate IX (a) and (d).
Diam 56mm
Nelthropp Collection

438 Reid & Co England HM 1807–8
Gold case. White enamel dial. Subsidiary
seconds dial. Steel loop hands.
Spring detent. Helical spring.
Compensation balance. Dust-cap.
There is a hole cut out of the back plate so
as to make the escape-wheel readily visible.
Signed 'Reid & Co London. 1808'.
Diam 53mm
Presented by Sir David Salomons Bt, 1924

439 Brockbanks England
HM 1810–11
Silver case. Oval loop pendant.
White enamel dial. Subsidiary seconds
dial. Gold spade hands.
Spring detent. Steel escape-wheel.
Three-arm compensation balance.
Signed 'Brockbanks London. No. 699'.
Diam 53mm
Atkins Bequest, 1898

440 Brockbanks England
HM 1812–13
Gold hunter case in four-colour gold with
chiselled floral ornament (a steel nib
moves sideways to open the cover over the
dial). There is complicated engine-
turning on the gold cuvette. Stamped WI.
Gold dial with sunk subsidiary seconds
dial. The centre is sunk, engine-turned,
and covered with translucent red enamel.
The hour ring is enamelled grey-blue.
Gold wavy hands.
Spring detent. Free-sprung helical spring.
Three-arm compensation balance with
sliding weights each clamped by two
tangential screws. Half-quarter repeater
on three gongs.
Signed 'Brockbanks London No 700'.
See Clutton & Daniels, *Watches*,
figs 411–13.
Diam 61mm
See also page 55

Nelthropp Collection
See also colour plate III

441 John Roger Arnold England
HM 1813–14
Silver case. White enamel dial.
Subsidiary seconds dial. Gold spade
hands.
Spring detent. Steel helical spring.
Two-arm z compensation balance.
Signed 'Jno. R. Arnold London Inv et
Fecit 2122'.
Diam 57mm
Presented by Samuel Barnett, 1935

442 James Moore French England
HM 1814–15
Gold hunter case. Gold dial. Matt
chapter ring with polished figures.
Engine-turned centre. Steel wavy hands.
Spring detent. Two-arm compensation
balance. Helical spring. Signed 'French
Royal Exchange London 1029' on the
dust-cap and movement.
With gold fob-chain and seal. There is a
retractable hook as a bed-hook.
French was a Freeman of the Clockmakers'
Company in 1810.
Diam 50mm
Presented by Mrs A.T. Collier, 1947

443 Ellicott & Taylor England
HM 1815–16
Gold engine-turned case. White enamel
dial. Subsidiary seconds dial. Gold spade
hands.
Spring detent. Helical spring.
Compensation balance. Signed 'Ellicott &
Taylor London 9462'.
With key and chain.
Edward Ellicott was a Freeman of the
Clockmakers' Company 1795, Master and
died 1835. Taylor was a maker of lever
escapement watches combining a number
of unusual features. He went into
partnership with Ellicott c1805 and there
exists a similar lever watch with their joint
signatures. Otherwise nothing is known
about him.
Diam 56mm
Presented by Sir David Salomons Bt, 1924

444 Juvet & Cie Hong Kong and
Switzerland HM 1815
Gold engine-turned case with English
hallmark.
Enamel dial. Subsidiary seconds dial.
Pivoted detent. Fully jewelled Swiss bar
movement. Signed on plate and dome
'Juvet et Cie à Hong Kong'.
Diam 47mm
Bequeathed by T. Vickery, 1946

445 Barrauds England HM 1816–17
Silver pair-case, Earnshaw-type spring
detent. Balance and helical spring c1850.
Signed 'Barrauds Cornhill London 777'.
Diam 56mm
This watch was used with success in 1814
during the surveys of 'British North
America'.
Diams 57 and 52mm
See C. Jagger, *P.P. Barraud*, p 130

446 John Barwise England
HM 1821–2
Gold engine-turned case.
Gold dial with polished hour figures.
Subsidiary seconds dial. Steel spade
hands. Spring detent, flat spiral balance-
spring. Compensation balance.
Signed 'Barwise London 8327'.
Diam 53mm
Nelthropp Collection

447 Parkinson & Frodsham England
HM 1823–4
Silver case.
Spring detent. Flat spiral balance-spring
with its stud on a flexible arm to aid the
even coiling and uncoiling of the balance-
spring. Signed 'Parkinson & Frodsham
London 948'.
Diam 53mm
See also page 56
Presented by the Lords Commissioners of
the Admiralty, 1906

448 Breguet et Fils France c1830
Silver case. Brass cuvette signed
'Breguet et Fils 5077'.
Silvered dial. Subsidiary seconds dial.
Steel Breguet hands. Spring detent.
Two-arm compensation balance. Helical
spring with terminal curves.
Signed 'Breguet et Fils N 5077'.
Diam 56mm
See also page 56
Presented by the Lords Commissioners of
the Admiralty, 1906

449 Alexander Watkins England
1851
Gold engraved case.
Gold dial with four-colour gold
decoration. Steel hands. Day-of-month
dial.
Spring detent. Quarter-striking
clock-watch and repeater striking on five
gongs. Eight-day movement.
Signed 'Alexr. Watkins, City Road 1851.
London'.
The watch was made for the Great
Exhibition of 1851.
Diam 53mm
See also page 56

450 **F. Berguer** England HM 1855
Silver engine-turned case with dust-cap
signed 'Berguer, Holborn'.
Stamped HW. Enamel dial. Subsidiary
seconds dial.
Spring detent. Flat spiral spring.
Compensation balance. Dumb quarter
repeater with unusual pendant push.
Signed 'F. Berguer, Holborn. London
No 361'.
Diam 54mm
Collinson Collection

451 **Henry Dent-Gardner** England
HM 1873
Gold hunter case with crest in inlaid
coloured enamel on outer cover.
Stamped GAP. Enamel dial. Centre
seconds. Up-and-down dial.
Spring detent. Compensation balance.
'Duo-in-Uno' spring. Half-plate
movement.
Signed 'H. Dent Gardner London'.
Diam 51mm
Presented by D.E. Buckney, 1952

452 **Girard Perregaux** Switzerland
HM 1879–80
Gold engraved case with English hallmark.
Stamped 51701 and 14961.
White enamel dial. Gold hands.
Tourbillon with pivoted detent. Bar
movement. Going barrel. Spiral spring
with overcoil and regulator. Keyless
wound.
Signed on dial, movement and gold dome
'Girard Perregaux. Chaux de Fonds.
Cronometro Tourbillon'.
The movement was made by Ernest
Guinand for the Spanish market.
Diam 56mm
See also page 56
Nelthropp Collection

453 **Thomas Mercer** England
HM 1883–4
Gold case.
White enamel dial with subsidiary
seconds dial and up-and-down dial.
Spring detent and keyless wound fusee.
No signature.
Diam 50mm
See also page 56
Bequeathed by the widow of Thomas
Mercer, 1936.

452a

452b

Watches with lever escapement

Examples of the lever escapement, from its formative years up to about 1805, are so rare that few collectors can ever aspire to own one, yet here are to be found at least half a dozen of the greatest variety and interest.

Although British makers were the true pioneers of the lever escapement, by 1805 it had been driven from the field. People who wanted a reasonably slim and accurate watch bought a duplex, and those who required the utmost accuracy had a chronometer. After 1805, for the next ten years at least, and effectively for the next twenty, the only British levers were rack levers, of which the Collection has a representative collection. This was really no more than a final manifestation of Huygens' pirouette.

When the British re-introduced the lever in the 1820s it was in relatively cheap watches, either with the single-roller, crank-roller, Massey's or Savage's escapements. Only in the hands of one or two exceptional artists, such as Viner and Cummins, did British levers much before 1840 have compensation balances. It therefore seems fairly clear that lever makers of the '20s and '30s thought of the escapement as being better than a cylinder and more robust and cheaper than a duplex. It was not until 1850 that the firms of Frodsham and Dent once more gave British lever watches their deserved reputation, with three-quarter plate movements, compensation balance (sometimes free-sprung) and single-roller escapement. Dent was early in the field with a full keyless winding and hand-setting mechanism, realistically coupled with a going barrel. Some makers on the other hand contrived, not entirely satisfactorily, to combine keyless winding with a fusee.

In the meantime, the double-roller lever escapement as used today in all modern watches was being developed by Abraham-Louis Breguet. He had started experimenting with the escapement almost as early as had the British and by 1791 had arrived at a thoroughly satisfactory layout. Like the London pioneers he used no draw, but his levers were so wonderfully light that they performed satisfactorily without it, and it was not until about 1815 that he (or probably anyone else except Leroux) introduced it into his watches. By this time Breguet had arrived at the modern lever escapement for all practical purposes. At the end of the eighteenth century he also invented the tourbillon, and while he applied several escapements to it, it is his lever tourbillon watches which seem to have the most consistent performance.

*   *   *   *   *

The Collection provides a fairly complete chronological picture of the development of the lever escapement, but it is the score of outstanding watches, especially those made before 1805, that make this section of the Collection so exceptionally important.

It is well known that Thomas Mudge made the first pocket watch with a lever escapement in 1769 and that this watch has always been owned by our Royal Family. Pierre Le Roy seems to have made an isolated experiment, apparently in the mid 1770s, after which no one attempted it until in 1782 the London-based Swiss emigré Josiah Emery was persuaded by Count von Bruhl to make watches with the lever escapement. He seems to have produced about three a year over the next fifteen years; but the chronology of the survivors is very difficult to establish, since the hallmarks and his serial numbering provide no consecutive picture.

454a

454b

454c

For the first nine years he followed Mudge's layout with the two impulse pallets, and the forks of the lever at different levels. Then, in 1791, he changed over to a cranked roller escapement. Of the first type the Collection possesses no example, but there is a fine watch with the cranked-roller escapement, and Emery's characteristic regulator-type dial, in a gold case hallmarked 1792, which is illustrated (catalogue number 455).

Although Emery is certainly the most important of the early lever makers because he made far more of them than anyone else, and at least a dozen survive, far more important technically is John Leroux by whom only two watches survive, of which the British Museum has one and this Collection the other (catalogue number 454, illustrated). Whereas Emery was content to copy Arnold's 's' balance, Leroux used a very light wheel more like an Arnold 'oz'. His escapement has the peculiarity that all the lift is on the teeth of the escape-wheel. In this way he was able to secure equal lift and locking to which he added the invaluable safety measure of a very small recoil or 'draw'. In this he anticipated all other makers by about thirty years. For his balance-spring he employed the sophisticated tapered helical shape which has the advantage over a plain helix that adjacent coils cannot so easily touch each other. Therefore, although his immediate influence was slight, it was Leroux, more than anyone else among the pioneers of the lever escapement, who foresaw most surely the lines on which it was to develop. The hands of the Leroux watch are of flat, burnished gold, and in the illustration the hour hand has reflected so much light that it seems almost not to be there. It has an arrow head and a plain circle at the end of the tail.

A very few years younger than the rest of the British pioneers was John Grant, and through the generosity of his son the Collection has by far the greatest proportion of his surviving work. He became a Freeman of the Clockmakers' Company in 1781 and died in 1810, but he does not seem to have become involved with the lever escapement until about 1788, and most of his lever watches date from nearer the turn of the century or just afterwards. All display a strong experimental streak and are very well finished.

The oldest Grant lever in the Collection is catalogue number 456 (illustrated) which is in a gold case hallmarked 1795. It has a double-roller escapement and an advanced type of four-arm compensation balance with a helical spring and end-curves. Grant did not employ draw but he evidently placed great reliance on very deep locking of the lever pallets on the escape-wheel. In order to achieve this he commonly made escape-wheels with teeth projecting vertically from the rim of the wheel, as is done in this instance.

The next Grant is an obviously experimental piece which survives as a movement and was probably never cased. This is catalogue number 460, also illustrated. It has the cranked-roller escapement which Grant came to prefer, and the same vertical-toothed escape-wheel as number 456 above. Its peculiarity lies in its having two (uncompensated) balance-wheels, geared together, each with its own spiral spring. The regulators are arranged to act simultaneously. The movement is unnumbered and signed 'J.G. May 1800'. Finally, catalogue number 461 (illustrated), a gold-cased watch hallmarked for 1804, seems to be about his last word on the subject. As far as is known, two others survive; one in the British Museum and one in private ownership. The dial is the most striking and elegant of Grant's variants, the chapter ring being displaced slightly towards the XII so that the minutes ring almost exactly bisects the seconds ring, which is of the maximum diameter.

The escape-wheel is laid out like the escape-wheel of an ordinary verge escapement and similarly is driven by a contrate wheel. The lever, pivoted between the plates in the ordinary way, has its anchor arms at two different levels, playing to and fro across the plane of the escape-wheel. Deep locking without draw and equal locking and impulse were doubtless the object of this strange exercise which has come to be known as 'Grant's chaff-cutter'. However, the escapement also is of an unusual kind used by Mudge for his first lever escapement clock now in the British Museum (but not in his lever watch), and by various others subsequently, including Pendleton, and Breguet in the famous 'Marie Antoinette' watch and a few others. The 'fork' takes the form of a loop which encircles the balance-staff and has its fork-pins on the far side of the balance from the escape-wheel. The object presumably was to minimise engaging and disengaging friction but conversely it extended the escapement arc. After this tour de force it is sad to find Grant joining the general abandonment of the lever escapement and the only other watch by him in the Collection is an ordinary rack lever movement dating probably from about 1808, two years before his death.

The Collection is equally fortunate in possessing one of Breguet's very early levers, catalogue number 457 (illustrated). In common with catalogue number 461, by Grant, the fork is a loop encircling the balance-staff. It is an extremely difficult watch to date and the famous Breguet workshop records are frequently unhelpful over very early watches. The fractional numbering which ended in 1788 presents no great problems; nor does the series which started in 1787 with the famous thirty 'perpetuelles' and continued to number 220 in 1793 when the Gide partnership broke up and Breguet started the numbering series which continued until after his death. There are however several watches which have all the appearance of being very early pieces which perhaps were put aside when Gide came into the business in 1787. In 1794, after he had (apparently amicably) withdrawn his capital, Breguet may well have been short of money and therefore glad to take out these early *ébauches* and finish them. To this category may well belong the present number 125 to which is added the mysterious fraction of $\frac{9}{4}$.

There is one other watch (last heard of in America but now untraceable) which has an inexplicable fraction and seems to date from about the same period as this one. As mentioned in the catalogue entry, the watch contains other anomalous features. On the whole, it may be safe to date it as started before the Revolution and finished about 1795.

Breguet's other lever watch in the Collection (catalogue number 469, illustrated) is one of his famous tourbillons. Like some other Breguet tourbillons it is absolutely devoid of ornament and the movement is not even signed (the tourbillon *ébauches* seem nearly all to have been made for Breguet by Houriet). The full description of the watch under the catalogue entry need not be repeated here, but its most unexpected feature is that it contains his earliest form of lever escapement, probably perfected by 1787 and certainly by 1791 at latest. His very next number, 2572, also a tourbillon, in private ownership, has a single-roller escapement, which seems to be the earliest recorded example of this layout.

Breguet had in fact somewhat lost interest in the lever escapement at this time (about 1795–1815) and he was experimenting with a number of escapements including the Robin, and double Robin, or as he called it, his *échappement naturel*. It was only in about 1815, when he produced his completely modern, double-roller escapement, that he resumed the lever escapement in any large way. The present watch is therefore particularly interesting.

469a

469b

After these pioneer watches the student may trace almost every stage of the lever escapement through the rest of the nineteenth century, but Richard Dover Statter's and Thomas Statter's very high-grade 'Decimal Timekeeper' deserves attention (catalogue number 493, illustrated).

Pieces of marked individual merit and interest begin to appear once more at the end of the century. Among these is an American Ingersoll 'Yankee', number 503, which was made for Ingersoll by the Waterbury Company and sold in immense quantities from 1890 at one dollar each.

Tourbillon watches of the highest quality continued to be made in small numbers throughout the century and later, but the escapement demands exceedingly precise workmanship. In 1894 Bahne Bonniksen took out a patent for a much less exacting form of revolving escapement which he called the 'karrusel'. Breguet's tourbillon platforms mostly turned once a minute although there exist a few with four, and even six minute rotations. But the karrusels mostly took $52\frac{1}{2}$ minutes and the most rapid took 35. This was almost if not quite as effective as the tourbillon in eliminating position errors and for many years karrusel watches gained the highest marks in the Kew trials. The Collection possesses what must be one of the first ever made, signed by Brockbank, Atkins & Moore, under patent, and hallmarked 1894, the year of the patent (catalogue number 502). Another is a fine example by S. Smith & Son, hallmarked 1897, with its Kew Class 'A' Certificate (catalogue number 504, illustrated).

Smiths and Frodshams also produced one-minute lever tourbillons which were all made by Nicole Nielsen, and there is a superb example by Smith (catalogue number 506, illustrated). These twentieth-century British tourbillon and karrusel watches not only perform to a very close rate but, more importantly, sustain it over a longer period than probably any other form of watch with a mechanical escapement. The final example is the historic Smiths wristwatch worn by Sir Edmund Hillary, during the first successful ascent of Mount Everest in 1953 and presented to the Collection by him (catalogue number 515).

Lever escapement
(including rack lever)

454 John Leroux England
HM 1785–6
Gold pair-case. Stirrup pendant. White enamel dial. Signed 'Leroux London'. Subsidiary dials for hours and seconds. Central minute hand. Gold hands. Full-plate movement. All the impulse is given by the inclines on the teeth of the steel escape-wheel, which are hook-shaped, to pointed pallets on the lever. The short lever is placed tangentially to the escape-wheel. The pallets embrace only two teeth of the escape-wheel. A jewel set in the tail of the lever moves between the adjustable banking pins. The balance staff has a cranked roller for impulse and unlocking, and a separate

roller for the safety-dart. The escapement is provided with draw and so far as can be ascertained, Leroux was the only eighteenth-century maker of the lever escapement to employ draw. The balance is a four-arm steel wheel with timing screws and with two bi-metallic arms fixed to it, with stops to limit their outward movement (these have been taken incorrectly as a form of auxiliary compensation). The free-sprung balance-spring is conical in shape. The movement has a stop lever. Fusee. This is the earliest example of the lever escapement in the Collection. Signed 'J. Leroux Charg. Cross London' (there is no serial number).
Leroux was a Freeman of the Clockmakers' Company in 1781.
Diams 58 and 50mm

See page 63
See also: P.M. Chamberlain, *It's About Time*, pp 48–50; *Antiquarian Horology*, June 1956, p 166; Clutton & Daniels, *Watches*, p 116 and figs 47 and 303–4
Presented by Admiral Lord Lyons, 1859
Illustrated on page 63

455 Josiah Emery England
HM 1792–3
Gold case.
White enamel dial. Signed 'Emery London'. Subsidiary dials for hours and seconds. Central minute hand. Steel hands. Full-plate movement with bridge-cock. The layout of the lever is straight-line. The escapement is without draw. The balance-staff has a cranked roller for impulse and unlocking and there is a separate safety roller. (This watch is one of

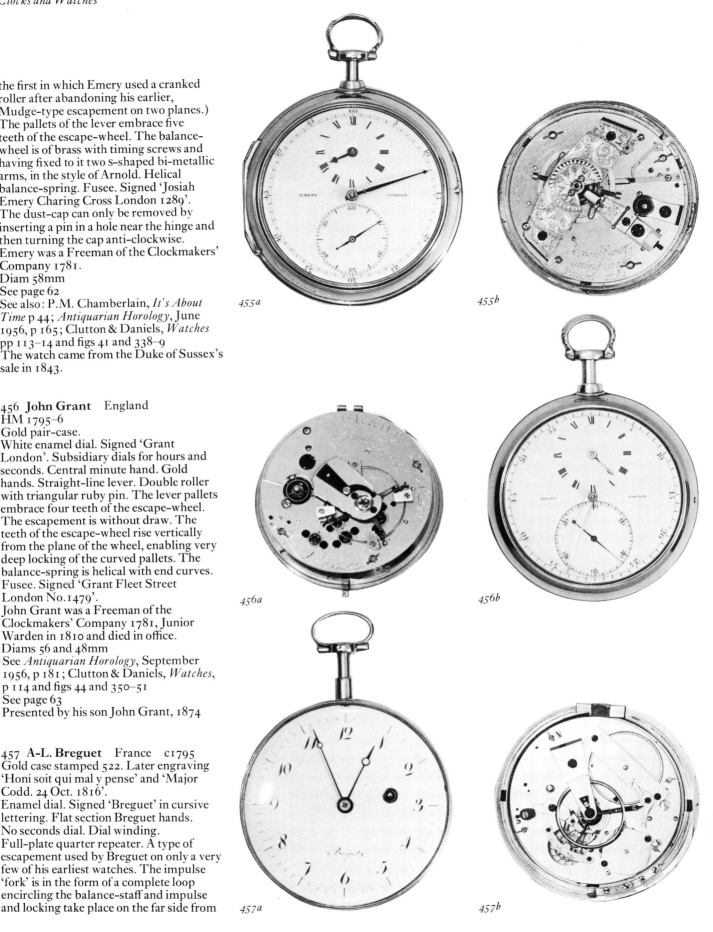

the first in which Emery used a cranked
roller after abandoning his earlier,
Mudge-type escapement on two planes.)
The pallets of the lever embrace five
teeth of the escape-wheel. The balance-
wheel is of brass with timing screws and
having fixed to it two s-shaped bi-metallic
arms, in the style of Arnold. Helical
balance-spring. Fusee. Signed 'Josiah
Emery Charing Cross London 1289'.
The dust-cap can only be removed by
inserting a pin in a hole near the hinge and
then turning the cap anti-clockwise.
Emery was a Freeman of the Clockmakers'
Company 1781.
Diam 58mm
See page 62
See also: P.M. Chamberlain, *It's About
Time* p 44; *Antiquarian Horology*, June
1956, p 165; Clutton & Daniels, *Watches*
pp 113–14 and figs 41 and 338–9
The watch came from the Duke of Sussex's
sale in 1843.

455a   *455b*

456 **John Grant**   England
HM 1795–6
Gold pair-case.
White enamel dial. Signed 'Grant
London'. Subsidiary dials for hours and
seconds. Central minute hand. Gold
hands. Straight-line lever. Double roller
with triangular ruby pin. The lever pallets
embrace four teeth of the escape-wheel.
The escapement is without draw. The
teeth of the escape-wheel rise vertically
from the plane of the wheel, enabling very
deep locking of the curved pallets. The
balance-spring is helical with end curves.
Fusee. Signed 'Grant Fleet Street
London No.1479'.
John Grant was a Freeman of the
Clockmakers' Company 1781, Junior
Warden in 1810 and died in office.
Diams 56 and 48mm
See *Antiquarian Horology*, September
1956, p 181; Clutton & Daniels, *Watches*,
p 114 and figs 44 and 350–51
See page 63
Presented by his son John Grant, 1874

456a   *456b*

457 **A-L. Breguet**   France   c1795
Gold case stamped 522. Later engraving
'Honi soit qui mal y pense' and 'Major
Codd. 24 Oct. 1816'.
Enamel dial. Signed 'Breguet' in cursive
lettering. Flat section Breguet hands.
No seconds dial. Dial winding.
Full-plate quarter repeater. A type of
escapement used by Breguet on only a very
few of his earliest watches. The impulse
'fork' is in the form of a complete loop
encircling the balance-staff and impulse
and locking take place on the far side from

457a   *457b*

the escape-wheel. Divided lift. Brass balance and compensation curb.
Signed on the dust-cap 'Breguet no 125' and on the brass rim round the dial 'Breguet No. $125\frac{9}{4}$'.
This watch is one of a small number which seem to have been started before 1787 and put aside until some time about 1792. The fractional numbering does not fit in with the form of fractional numbering used by Breguet before 1788, but there are a few other, apparently random fractional numbers whose significance has not so far been interpreted. The case of this watch may have been intended for another movement, as it had originally a hole for winding in the back, with a secret shutter, but this has been subsequently filled in and the watch is dial-wound.
Diam 55mm
See page 64
Collinson Collection

458 John Johnston   Scotland
Late 18th century.
Movement only. Damaged enamel dial and hands.
Quarter repeating movement with later conversion to lever escapement.
Signed 'Jnº Johnston. Ayr. 282'.
Diam 46mm
Collinson Collection

459 Jean Antoine Lepine   France
Late 18th century.
Silver engine-turned English case with hallmark 1831–2.
White enamel dial with Arabic hour figures and minute figures in red.
Signed 'Lepine invenit et fecit'. Gold fleur-de-lys hands. Steel centre seconds hand above the other hands.
The movement was probably originally a virgule but was converted at an early date to lever with an escapement similar to Breguet's first type, but with a very short lever. The going barrel has no cock.
Signed on the cuvette 'Lepine Hger du Roy A Paris 5230'.
Diam 56mm
Presented by Francis B. Adams, 1870

460 John Grant   England   1800
Movement only. White enamel dial. The balance-staff has a cranked roller and the escape-wheel has raised teeth with which the curved face of the lever pallets lock deeply. There are two balance-wheels, geared together by wheels of 80 teeth, and each having a spiral balance-spring. Fusee.
Signed 'J.G. London May 1800'.
Diam 38mm
See page 63
See also Clutton & Daniels, *Watches*, pp 41 and 114 and fig 46
Presented by his son John Grant, 1850

461 John Grant   England
HM 1804–5
Gold case. White enamel dial. The eccentric hour circle overlaps the seconds dial. Gold arrow hands.
The escapement is of the kind generally known as 'Grant's chaff-cutter'. The escape-wheel is at right angles to the plates and is driven by a contrate wheel. The lever has its pallets in two planes working to and fro across the plane of the escape-wheel. The 'fork' of the escapement is in the form of a loop encircling the balance staff, impulse and locking taking place on the far side of the escape-wheel. The two-arm compensation balance has sliding weights. The balance-spring is helical without end-curves. No draw. Signed on movement and dust-cap 'Grant Fleet Street London 2802'.
Diam 61mm
See page 63
See also: P.M. Chamberlain, *It's About Time*, pp 74, 75, with line drawing of the escapement; *Antiquarian Horology*, September 1956, p 181; Clutton & Daniels, *Watches*, pp 41 and 114.
Presented by his son John Grant, 1874

462 John Grant   England   c1808
Movement only. White enamel dial. Gold spade hands.
Rack lever. Steel balance. Solid cock with 'Patent' on foot. Signed 'Grant Fleet Strt. London 3394'.
Diam 42mm
Nelthropp Collection

460

461a

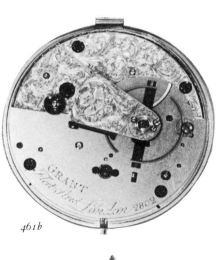
461b

461c

463 Louis Recordon England
HM 1807–8
Gold engine-turned case. Flat edge-band with engine-turning. White enamel dial. Subsidiary seconds dial. Signed 'Recordon late Emery. London'. Moon hands. The lever escapement is certainly a later conversion as is the jewelling throughout and the index regulator and scale. Compensation balance. Signed 'Recordon late Emery. Cockspur St. Charing Cross London No.7392'.
Diam 43mm
Presented by the Executors of Mrs Du Pasquier

464 Thomas Earnshaw England
Early 19th century.
Movement only. White enamel dial. Subsidiary seconds dial. No hands. Lever escapement is a later conversion; presumably originally spring detent. Two-arm compensation balance. Helical balance-spring. Fusee. Signed 'Thos. Earnshaw Invt. et Fecit 436. London No.2726'.
Earnshaw's system of double numbering is not understood.
Diam 53mm
Presented by Messrs A. & J. Smith, 1928

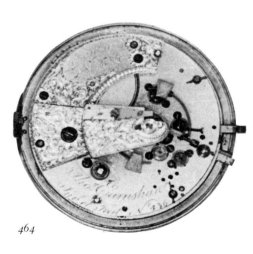

464

465 [Breguet] Probably Swiss
Early 19th century
Gold case.
Tavan type of pin-wheel lever escapement. Falsely signed 'Breguet' but a fine watch.

466 John Barwise England
HM 1809–10
Gold case hallmarked. Bezel and movement both on a hinge opposite the pendant.
White enamel dial. Subsidiary seconds dial. Gold arrow hands.
Rack lever. Steel balance. Dust-cap. Signed 'Barwise London No 4791'.
Diam 53mm
Nelthropp Collection

467 Litherland & Co England c1810
Movement only.
Rack lever. Foot of cock engraved 'Patent'. Signed 'Litherland & Co. Liverpool No.3435'.
Bequeathed by T. Vickery, 1946

468 French England HM 1811–12
Silver early hunter case.
Enamel dial. Subsidiary seconds dial. Gold spade hands. Dust-cap.
Rack lever. Plain steel balance. Diamond endstone and very large ruby jewels to escape, 4th and 3rd wheels. Cock engraved 'Patent'. Signed 'French Royal Exchange London 671' (probably Edward French).
Diam 56mm
Presented by John W. Carter, 1908

469 A-L. Breguet France 1812
Silver case. Back engine-turned with central space having an engraved crown covered with colourless transparent enamel. Stamped 2571 and 281. White enamel dial. Subsidiary seconds dial. Breguet hands. Dial signed in cursive lettering 'Breguet', and secret signature 'Breguet et Fils No 2571'. One-minute tourbillon with Breguet's first type of lever escapement. The two pins on the lever, serving as the fork, are gold and the safety dart is steel. The impulse pallet is jewelled. Two-arm compensation balance with countersunk screws. Spiral spring with overcoil, free-sprung. Signed on silver cuvette 'Breguet et Fils. Regulateur à Tourbillon no.2571'.
Fusee.
With short silver chain and key.
Diam 58mm
See page 64
See also *Antiquarian Horology*, September 1956, p 182; Sir David Salomons, *Breguet* (Watch number 81).
The watch was sold in 1812 to the Princesse de Valençay. It was presented by Sir David Salomons Bt.
Illustrated on page 64

470 Peter Litherland & Co England
HM 1813–14
Silver pair-case.
White enamel dial. Subsidiary seconds dial. Gold arrow hands.
Rack lever. Ruby endstone. Steel balance Signed 'Peter Litherland & Co. Liverpool No.662'.
Diams 55 and 48mm

471 Septimus Miles England
HM 1814
Gold pair-case stamped DW.
Gold engine-turned dial. Subsidiary seconds dial. Gold hands.
Rack lever. Flat steel balance-wheel. Stop lever. Signed on movement and dust-cap 'Sept⁵ Miles Ludgate Street London 4820'.
Diams 56 and 50mm
Collinson Collection

472 James McCabe Junior England HM 1815–16
Gold hunter case, engine-turned. Gold dial engine-turned. Subsidiary seconds dial. Steel loop hands. Lever escapement conversion from cylinder or duplex. Signed 'Jas. McCabe Royal Exchange London 7972'.
Diam 53mm
Bequeathed by Sir Jamsetjee Jejeebhoy Bt, 1898

473 Morris Tobias England c1820
Movement only.
Rack lever. Compensation curb. Scallop-shaped cock-foot engraved 'Patent'. Signed 'Morris Tobias London No. 967'.
Bequeathed by T. Vickery, 1946

474 Charles Brandt England c1820
Movement only. Escape-wheel of 28 teeth. Steel balance.
Signed 'Cha⁵ Brandt. London. A.L. 5817'.
Presented by John W. Carter, 1908

475 Robert Roskell England c1820
Movement only. Enamel dial (damaged) with alarm dial. The alarm is set through the foot of the cock and winds by a starwheel. Signed 'Robᵗ Roskell. Liverpool 21486' and on cock foot 'Patent 84'.
This movement evidently came out of a clock.
Diam 50mm
Bequeathed by T. Vickery, 1946

476 William Brown England
HM 1820
Gold engine-turned hunter case with
carved band, pendant and ring.
Stamped WM.
Gold engine-turned dial. Subsidiary
seconds dial. Fusee. Dust-cap.
Single-roller lever. Jewelled movement.
Signed 'Will.ᵐ Brown
London No 4615'

477 Barrauds England HM 1822–3
Gold pair-case.
White enamel dial. Subsidiary seconds
dial. Gold spade hands. Savage two-pin
lever with trapezoidal pin. Ruby endstone.
Brass balance. Fusee. Signed 'Barrauds
Cornhill London 2/1491'.
Diams 55 and 50mm
See C. Jagger, *P.P. Barraud*, p 144
Nelthropp Collection

478 John Roger Arnold England
c1823
Movement only. White enamel dial
signed 'Arnold' in Gothic script.
Single roller lever. Prest's keyless winding
mechanism. Going barrel. Plain balance
with compensation curb. Signed
'Jnᵒ. R. Arnold London No $\frac{B}{184}$ Patent'
Diam 48mm
Collinson Collection

479 Richard Ganthony England
HM 1823–4
Gold case, engine-turned, with chiselled
border and bezel.
Dial in four-colour gold. Polished Arabic
numerals in relief. Wreath round centre.
Gold loop hands.
Brass balance. Single-roller lever.
Signed 'Ganthony 83 Cheapside London
No 3372'.
Ganthony was a Freeman of the
Clockmakers' Company 1794, Master
1828 and 1829, died 1845. The watch was
made for Mrs Jane Munro, widow of
Colonel R. Munro, of Madras Presidency.
Diam 45mm
Nelthropp Collection

480 John West Ireland HM 1824
Gold engine-turned case with carved
band, pendant and ring stamped HJ.4307.
Gold dial. Three-colour border.
Engine-turned centre. Subsidiary
seconds dial.
Crank-roller lever. Regulator on cock
table. Signed 'West. 9 Capel Street
Dublin 688'.
Diam 55mm

481 Dwerrihouse, Carter & Co
England HM 1824–5
Silver engine-turned case.
Silver engine-turned dial. Subsidiary
seconds dial. Steel loop hands.
Crank-roller. Very large escape-wheel with
vertical teeth. Very large balance. Fusee.
Signed 'Dwerrihouse, Carter & Co.
Davies Stt. Berkeley Square'.
Diam 54mm

482 G. Littlewort England c1825
Wood case reinforced with brass and a
lock.
White enamel dial. Gold hands.
Brass balance. Fusee. 3-day movement.
Signed on brass plate surrounding dial
'George Littlewort, 197, by the Kings
Letters Patent. London. General Post
Office. W.R.'.
Up to 1846 GPO mails were carried by
coach in the custody of the mail guard.
He was provided with a watch which was
set by a GPO official and then locked in its
box so that the hands could not be
tampered with. The guard had to report
the time of arrival and departure of the
mail coach at each stage of the journey,
the time being entered by the postmaster
on a time-bill.
Length 95mm

483 Haley & Son England c1830
Movement only. Silver dial, engine-
turned. Subsidiary seconds dial.
Signed 'Haley & Son'. Steel spade hands.
Compensation balance. Signed 'Haley &
Son. London $\frac{M}{MME}$'
Haley was succeeded by James Grohé at
7 Wigmore Street in 1834.
Diam 48mm
Presented by Evan Roberts, 1912

484 J. Pickford England c1830
Movement only. Half-plate movement.
Steel balance. Signed 'J. Pickford
Liverpool. 1980'.
Diam 40mm
Collinson Collection

485 John Foster England
HM 1832
Gold engine-turned case with carved
floral edges. Chester hallmark.
Stamped TE. Gold rayed dial with
two-colour gold floral border.
Plain steel balance.
Signed 'Jnᵒ. Foster Liverpool No. 2724'.
Diam 40mm
Collinson Collection

486 Abraham Jackson England
HM 1838
Gold engine-turned case with carved band.
Stamped $\frac{T.H.}{J.H.}$. Chester hallmark.
Three-colour gold dial. Subsidiary
seconds dial.
Plain steel balance. Three very large
jewels. The lever pivots are in adjustable
potences. Signed 'Abᵐ Jackson
Liverpool 5105'.
Diam 55mm
Presented by Gilbert J. Innes, 1955

487 Arnold & Frodsham England
c1843
Movement only. Enamel dial. Subsidiary
seconds dial. Signed 'Arnold 7127'.
Gold spade hands.
Three-quarter plate movement. Brass
balance. Signed 'J.R. Arnold Chaˢ
Frodsham. 84 Strand London 7127'.
J.R. Arnold died in 1843 when the firm
was taken over by Charles Frodsham, so
this movement must be c1843.
Diam 38mm
Presented by John W. Carter, 1913

488 Charles & Hollister England
HM 1850
Silver case. Stamped $\frac{JB}{WW}$.
Silvered dial. Centre seconds and
independent seconds dial.
There are two trains, one operating the
independent seconds with a stop lever in
the bezels. Another stop lever stops the
going train. Signed on dial only 'Charles &
Hollister, makers, 27 Davies Street,
Berkeley Square'.
Diam 80mm
Collinson Collection

489 J.M. Tobias Probably Swiss
c1850
Gold case, chased and engine-turned.
Stamped 8920.
Enamel dial. Subsidiary seconds dial.
Bar movement. Plain steel balance.
Signed 'J.M. Tobias London'.
The watch and case are clearly of Swiss
origin.
J.M. Tobias is not recorded as a maker but
was probably a descendant of Tobias & Co
of London and Liverpool.
Diam 48mm
Presented by Mrs H.L. Barratt, 1970

490 Frederic Ate Perret Swiss
c1850
Gold engraved case stamped 29505 and
466.
Gold dial decorated with fine line

engraving. Centre seconds and subsidiary dials for time and seconds.
Multi-cock movement. There are two barrels. The watch beats seconds by means of a *fouet* or whip.
Signed 'Frederic Ate Perret aux Brenets'.
Diam 51mm
See Jaquet & Chapuis, *The Swiss Watch*, p 184.
Collinson Collection

491 Barraud & Lund England HM 1853
Silver hunter case engine-turned. Stamped AT.
Enamel dial signed 'Barraud & Lund $\frac{2}{6243}$'.
Brass balance. Signed 'Barraud & Lund Cornhill London $\frac{2}{6243}$'.
Diam 51mm
See C. Jagger, *P. P. Barraud*, p 146
Collinson Collection

492 Anonymous England c1860
Case of German silver with Royal Arms engraved on the back and number 82.
Stamped WB. Enamel dial.
Said to be a Post Office Mail Guard watch. A small screw passes through the pendant into the push-piece and prevents the watch being opened after time is set.
Diam 63mm
Nelthropp Collection

493 Richard Dover Statter & Thomas Statter England 1862
Gold case. Stamped GR.
White enamel dial inscribed 'Decimal Timekeeper'. Ordinary hour and minute dial below. Main dial is divided into 10 hours, each divided into 10. At the top is 'V noon' at the right, between II and III is 'Morning'; at the bottom is 'X Midnight'; at the left is 'Evening between VII and VIII. Centre seconds, the minute being divided into 100 seconds. The hands move anti-clockwise.
Compensation balance. Fusee. Signed 'Richd. Dover Statter & Thos. Statter, Liverpool No. 1' and on the gold dome 'The true basis of a universal Decimal system'.
Diam 53mm
See also page 65
There is a pamphlet in the Company's library by Dover Statter on the decimal system.

494 John Hornby England c1868
Silver case with reeded band stamped J.D. Hallmark not legible.
Enamel dial. Subsidiary seconds dial. Compensation balance of Earnshaw type. Spiral balance-spring.
Signed 'John Hornby. Liverpool 224'.
Diam 46mm
Collinson Collection

495 [Bovet] Switzerland c1870
Silver case. Glazed back. Stamped LF 4519/8 and Chinese characters.
White enamel dial with Chinese numerals. Steel hands and centre seconds. Single roller lever with extended tail. Going barrel. Signed on oval plate on movement in Chinese. The mechanism is elaborately engraved and jewelled and is attributed with confidence to Les Frères Bovet (Albert and Charles) at Fleurier.
Diam 53mm
See A. Chapuis, *La Montre Chinoise*, p 157 and Fig 121.
Bequeathed by M.L. Bateman, 1966

496 Cozens, Matthews & Thorpe England c1870
Movement only. Enamel dial numbered 100601.
Compensation balance. Spiral balance-spring. Jewelled. Signed 'Cozens, Matthews & Thorpe, 10 Bunhill Row London 100601'.
Diam 42mm
Presented by Evan Roberts, 1912

497 George Blackie England 1873
Gold engine-turned case. White enamel dial. Subsidiary seconds and up-and-down dials.
Helical balance-spring. Signed 'Geoe. Blackie fecit 392 Strand London No 742' and engraved on back plate 'Nelthropp prize winner 1873'.
Diam 48mm
Presented by G.W. Atkins, 1929

498 Robert W. Goddard England HM 1880–1
Gold engraved case. Gold engraved dial. Signed on back plate 'Robt W. Goddard 61 Packington Street London 1328'.
Diam 41mm
Presented by W.R. Corke, Master of the Clockmakers' Company 1923, by whom the engraving was executed

499 Sir John Bennett England HM 1884
Gold case. Stamped A. & 42972.
Enamel dial. Subsidiary seconds dial. Three-quarter plate. Keyless wind.
Signed 'Sir John Bennett 65 & 64 Cheapside. London. 42972'.
Diam 48mm
Collinson Collection

493a

493b

500 W.N. Vokes Anglo-Swiss 1887
Gold half-hunter case. Dome inscribed
'Made by W.N. Vokes at the Horological
School Geneva 1887'.
Swiss lever escapement. Quarter repeater.
Jewelled throughout.
Diam 53mm
Presented by W.N. Vokes, 1932

501 R.W. Whittaker England
HM 1889–90
Silver case. White enamel dial.
Subsidiary seconds dial.
Resilient lever escapement with
compensation balance. Signed
'R.H. Whittaker 46 Wilton Road
Victoria SW 12/1890'.
Whittaker's patent for the escapement is
No 13794 of 1888. The fork and safety
roller are mounted on a spring attached to
the lever. The fork also has chamfered
outer edges over which the impulse pin
could ride under shock conditions.
Diam 53mm
Nelthropp Collection

502 Brockbank, Atkins & Moore
England HM 1894
Silver case. White enamel dial.
Subsidiary seconds dial.
Karrusel movement revolving in $52\frac{1}{2}$
minutes. Signed 'Brockbank, Atkins &

Moore. Cowper's Ct. Cornhill, London
No. 8–1823 Patent 21421'.
The patent quoted is that taken out by
Bahne Bonniksen in 1894 for his karrusel
mechanism. This watch must therefore be
one of the earliest karrusel watches to be
made or to have survived.
Diam 59mm
See also page 65
Nelthropp Collection

503 Ingersoll America c1896
Case of brass silver-plated.
White card dial signed 'Yankee. R.H.
Ingersoll, New York'.
Pin pallet, Roskopf-type lever. There is a
false pendant button, the spring being
wound by a fixed winding button on the
back plate. Signed 'R.H. Ingersoll & Bro.
New York. U.S.A. Pat. May 6.
Dec. 23. 1890. Jan 13 1891. May 29. 1894'.
The 'Yankee' was a very early model of
Ingersoll and was the first watch to be sold
for one dollar. It was made by the
Waterbury Company in immense numbers
and marketed by the Ingersoll Brothers.
Diam 55mm (thickness 25mm)
See page 65
See also *Bulletin of the National
Association of Watch & Clock Collectors*,
(USA), Vol V, number 3, April 1952,
pp 97–110
Bequeathed by M.L. Bateman, 1966

504 S. Smith & Son England
HM 1897
Silver case with gold hinges. Stamped J.W.
White enamel dial inscribed 20794.
Steel hands.
Karrusel movement revolving in $52\frac{1}{2}$
minutes. Free-sprung. Single-roller lever.
Signed 'Kew Class A Certificate 70.4
marks. 20794. Watchmakers to the
Admiralty. S. Smith & Son. 9 Strand
London'.
For particulars of the Bonniksen
karrusel patent see number 502.
See also page 65
Presented by Smiths Industries Ltd, 1968

505 Anonymous England HM 1901
Gold case Birmingham hallmark.
Movement swings out on a hinge; a very
late example. Stamped WE 511086.
Enamel dial. Subsidiary seconds dial.
Three-quarter plate movement. Keyless
winding with winding pinion attached to
the outer case. Back plate unsigned but
numbered 511086.
Diam 49mm
Collinson Collection

506 S. Smith & Son England
HM 1907
Gold hunter case. Sheffield hallmark.
Dial silvered and numbered 302/8, also
'up and down' dial.
Three-quarter plate, one minute
tourbillon movement by Nicole Nielsen &
Co. Signed 'S. Smith & Son. 9 Strand.
London. No. 302/8'.
See also page 65
Diam 58mm
Presented by Smiths Industries Ltd, 1968
See next page for illustration

507 Anonymous Switzerland c1912
Silver case, the back embossed or chiselled
with a steam locomotive.
Venetian enamel dial inscribed
'*Régulateur*'. Filigree hands.
Swiss double roller lever.
The case of this watch is probably
embossed although *The Swiss Watch*,
plates 132 and 142, states that similar cases
were chiselled.
Diam 70mm
Presented by W.R. Fletcher, 1961

508 Hebdomas Switzerland c1927
Silver engine-turned case. Stamped GS
and Swiss date stamps.
Enamel dial with oval chapter ring.
Lower portion cut away to expose the
balance. 8-day movement. Signed on dial
'Hebdomas Patent 8 days Swiss Made'.
Diam 47mm
Collinson Collection

504a

504b

506a   *506b*

509 John Harwood England c1928
Silver 13-ligne wristwatch case. Stamped
ASM.8.925. 12026. Silvered dial.
Self-winding movement, 10½-ligne.
There is no winding stem, the hands being
set by rotating the milled bezel one way or
the other. A red spot appears in an aperture
on the dial when the bezel is in its neutral
position. Signed 'Harwood Self-winding
Watch Co. Ltd. Patent 1576120.
Cannon Street London EC4'.
An example of the first self-winding wrist-
watch made 1928–32 when the depression
forced liquidation. Mr John Harwood
made his first prototype in Douglas,
Isle of Man, in 1922. Eventually, the
Swiss firm of A. Schild & Co made the
ébauches for the English firm.
Diam 43mm
See: *Jeweller & Metal Worker*, July 15
1960; *Journal Suisse d'Horologerie et
Bijouterie*, May–June 1951; Chapuis &
Jaquet, *History of the Self-winding Watch*,
p 227.
Presented by I.F. Luckin, 1969

510 John Harwood England c1928
Movement only of Harwood self-winding
wristwatch. See number 509.
Diam 30mm
Presented by G.S. Sanders, 1970

511 Anonymous Switzerland c1935
Silver case with Swiss date marks.
Stamped GS 24519.
Enamel dial with subsidiary dials.
Split seconds chronograph movement.
Diam 53mm
Bequeathed by T. Vickery, 1946

512 Smiths English Clocks Ltd
England 1942
Stainless steel case. White enamel dial.
Movement 27mm diameter. Nickel
balance with Chronovar spring. 15 jewels.
A specimen of the first wristwatches made
in England by quantity production
methods.
Diam 30mm
Presented by Smiths Industries Ltd, 1948

513 Smiths English Clocks Ltd
England 1944
Chromium-plated case. White enamel
dial.
15-jewel movement. Nickel balance.
Chronovar spring.
A specimen of the first pocket-watch made
in England by quantity production
methods.
Diam 43mm
Presented by Smiths Industries Ltd, 1948

514 Ingersoll England 1947
Steel case.
Black and silver dial. Luminous hands.
Signed on dial 'Ingersoll Triumph'.
Diam 51mm
Bequeathed by M.L. Bateman. An
inscription on the back reads 'Presented to
Mr. M.L. Bateman, a Director of
Ingersoll Ltd., to commemorate the
Company's first production of an all
British pocket watch January 1947'.

515 Smiths English Clocks Ltd
England 1953
Steel waterproof wristwatch case by
Dennison Watch Case Co.
Silvered dial. Subsidiary seconds dial.
Signed on the dial 'Smiths De Luxe'.
15-jewel escapement.
See page 65
Presented by Sir Edmund Hillary
who wore the watch during his successful
climb to the summit of Mount Everest,
May 29th 1953

Watches with miscellaneous escapements

Every one of the twenty-four watches in this section is of technical interest. It may be argued that Haley's constant-force escapement (catalogue number 435) should have been included here but it was considered marginally qualified for classification as a detent escapement. It might be argued equally that catalogue number 537 (illustrated) should have been regarded as a detent escapement; but it seemed sufficiently eccentric to be regarded as 'miscellaneous'.

In catalogue number 539 (illustrated) is the only watch in the collection not possessing a mechanical escapement. This is a Bulova 'Accutron', presented by the makers in 1969. It relies on an electrically-energised tuning-fork vibrating 360 times a second to control the timekeeping. In 1963, the Company awarded their Tompion Gold Medal to Max Hetzel who was responsible for the development of this tuning-fork device as a time standard for a wristwatch. Only four awards of this medal have been made and Max Hetzel is the only one whose work is included in the Collection.

The invention of the virgule escapement is attributed variously to the French makers Lepine and Lepaute. In fact it was invented by Tompion, but although there is a contemporary description of such a watch by him, none has survived. From his original idea stemmed the cylinder and virgule escapements. The cylinder was, of course, developed by Graham, but the virgule in its developed form was the work of Lepine and Lepaute, though it was Lepine who did most to popularise the escapement. It has the theoretical advantage over the cylinder that locking takes place over a roller of smaller radius, while impulse is spread over a longer arc and with greater mechanical advantage. Its defect proved to be that it was impossible to keep oil in the escapement, without which it quickly destroyed itself. Lepine's watches are also interesting because it was he who introduced the ébauche with separate cocks, as opposed to the plated movement. He also frequently used ratchet-shaped teeth throughout the trains of his best watches, known as 'wolf's teeth'. He retired from business in 1789 but the firm continued to make high-grade watches, in which they liked to mix up Arabic and Roman numerals on the dials. Thus, for one reason or another, a Lepine watch is nearly always interesting. A Lepine movement (catalogue number 523, illustrated) has all these peculiarities and there is a second virgule in a non-original case (number 518). In a virgule escapement there is impulse in only one direction, but Beaumarchais devised the double virgule, which is really two virgule escapements mounted on top of each other, thereby arranging for impulse to be imparted in both directions. Catalogue number 526 is an example by Cronier.

Number 522 is an extremely strange arrangement. It is in effect a Robin escapement, in which the balance is impulsed by the escape-wheel which is then locked by a cylinder carried on the lever arbor. That is to say, the lever has an ordinary fork to engage the balance-staff; but instead of locking the escape-wheel by an ordinary anchor, a cylinder is mounted on the lever arbor and it is on this that locking takes place.

Numbers 533 and 534 are both examples of another strange mechanical aberration for which Thomas Smith of Coventry took out a patent in 1812 and number 533 is by Smith himself, of that year. The escape-wheel, driven by a contrate wheel, has five pin-shaped teeth at right angles to its rim, operating on a lever very much like a Grant chaff-cutter. The lever is geared to the balance by a rack and pinion. It is therefore strictly a rack lever escapement but it seemed sufficiently unusual to include in this section.

Finally come the various frictional rest escapements which almost defy any definitive form of classification. The names Debaufre, Sully, Flamenville, Enderlin, Ormskirk and Garnier may all be bandied about but there will still be variants which fit no single label. The only completely clear-cut case seems to be Sully's escapement which has a single ratchet-shaped escape-wheel operating on two pallets on the balance-staff, as demonstrated in Sully's marine timepiece number 597. But on the whole it has seemed safest to avoid labels altogether and briefly describe each variant, leaving the student who is sufficiently interested to examine them at leisure. This they certainly deserve, and the Collection is particularly well-furnished with varied examples of this relatively rare type of escapement.

Miscellaneous escapements
(including frictional rest escapements other than cylinder and duplex)

516 Jeremiah Martin   England
Early 18th century
Silver pair-case. Inner stamped RB.605.
Outer case covered tortoiseshell inlaid with silver studs and a Chinese scene.
Later dial. Minute hand missing.
Frictional rest escapement having an ordinary small verge-type escape-wheel acting on two conical discs on the balance-staff, which is offset to one side of the escape-wheel. Large balance with spring.
Silver plate on top plate engraved with signature 'Ieremiah Martin London'.
Martin was a Freeman of the Clockmakers' Company 1687.
The escapement is probably an early conversion from verge.
Diams 50 and 44mm

517 Markwick Markham   England
c1740
Movement only White enamel dial.
Steel beetle hands. Frictional rest escapement.
The escapement, which shows some signs of not being original, has a verge-type escape-wheel that acts on two pallets at about 90° to each other, cut through the balance-staff, which is mounted in line with the escape-wheel arbor. This escapement is sometimes described as a 'dead-beat verge' but it has in fact a small amount of recoil.
Silver balance-cock with a cherub's face instead of the usual gargoyle mask.
Ornate pillars. Signed 'Markwick Markham London 6826'.
Diam 35mm
See Charles Gros, *Echappements D' Horloges et de Montres*, (1913), fig 100;
Thomas Reid, *Treatise on Clock &*

Watchmaking, (1843), plate IX, fig 50;
P.M. Chamberlain, *It's About Time*, (1941, reprinted 1964), p 152, fig 26.
Presented by B.L. Vulliamy, 1816

518 Jean Antoine Lepine   France
c1780
Silver case, not original.
White enamel dial and gold loop hands, not original.
Single virgule escapement. Wolf's teeth train. Going barrel without cock. Signed 'Lepine Hger. du Roy A Paris N.1711'.
Diam 35mm
See also page 73
Nelthropp Collection

519 James Ryland   England   c1780
Movement only. White enamel dial.
Gold spade hands.
Frictional rest escapement having two co-axial verge-type escape-wheels with the teeth facing each other on opposite sides of the balance-staff on which is a single pallet. The watch is fitted with an adjustable back potence and the mainspring is held in place by a brass guard fixed to the back plate. Going barrel. Signed 'James Ryland Ormskirk 175'.
The Rylands evidently specialised in this escapement as there is a similar watch by Joshua Ryland, presumably son of James, see number 532.
Diam 35mm
Presented by Evan Roberts, 1893

520 Hugh Garrat   England   c1790
Movement only. White enamel dial.
Ornate Continental-type hands.
Frictional rest escapement. A single verge-type escape-wheel acts on two half-pallets on the balance-staff which is off-set at one side of the escape-wheel.
The wheel-pattern bridge-cock, as well as

the hands, have a Continental appearance so that it may be an imported movement.
There is no mainspring barrel, the spring being maintained by a brass guard.
Signed 'Hugh Garrat. Ormskirk No. 292'.
Diam 40mm

521 Berthoud   France   c1790
Pair-case. Outer formed of gilt bezels and glass. Inner gold case has the back enamelled in a figure scene in blue with oval gold border. The type of enamelling used gives a sunrise effect and is attained by the use of translucent enamel over rayed engine-turning and is known on the Continent as *à l'aurore*.
White enamel dial. No minute figures.
Gold loop hands. Dial winding.
Virgule escapement. Balance-rim in recess in top plate, level with the plate.
Going barrel. Very thin movement.
Signed 'Berthoud London'.
The signature is not understood. There is no record of the Berthouds having had a London establishment.
Diams 63 and 59mm

522 Anonymous   England   HM 1792
Silver case, hallmarked. It opens only from the back.
White enamel dial. Subsidiary seconds dial. No minute figures. Steel arrow hands.
The escapement is an unusual variety of Robin. On the balance-staff are the two usual pallets, one for receiving impulse and one for engaging the fork of a lever for locking the escape-wheel. However, locking is not achieved by the usual anchor but by a steel cylinder integral with the lever arbor. On the 'dead' beat, an escape-wheel tooth moves only from the outside to the inside of the cylinder.
Compensation curb of two straight and parallel bi-metallic strips with a very fine adjustment.

The watch was purchased from Brockbank & Atkins, who had owned it for most of its life.
Diam 71mm
See also page 73
Nelthropp Collection
See also illustration on page 77

523 Jean Antoine Lepine France
Late 18th century
Movement only. White enamel dial with hour figures 1. 2. 3. IV. V. VI. V2. V3. 9. X. 11. X2. Minute figures in red. Gold hands.
Virgule escapement. Cock for balance and one cock for the other three wheels. Going barrel without cock. 3rd and 4th wheels have a single steel end plate. All wheels have wolf's or ratchet teeth. Oil sinks throughout. Hinged cover to movement. Signed 'N.º 5407 Lepine Hger du Roy A Paris'.
Diam 50mm (Thickness 10mm)
See page 73
Presented by T.W. Jones, 1915

523a

523b

524 Anonymous Switzerland or France Late 18th century
Gold case. Back engine-turned and was originally covered with translucent enamel. Border of 58 half-pearls and outer white enamel ring. Bezel with similar border of 56 pearls. Square enamelled pendant stem. Movement with dial lifts out of the case and has hinged back cover.
White enamel dial. Gold loop hands. Virgule escapement. Going barrel without cock.
Diam 50mm
Presented by Samuel E. Atkins, 1893

525 Bompard France
Late 18th century
Movement only. Frictional rest escapement. Gilt dial with engine-turned centre. Hands missing. Silver bridge fusee. The escapement appears not to be original. It is similar to the two-wheel duplex but has two small co-axial escape-wheels with ratchet-shaped teeth which are not staggered. Impulse is delivered in one direction only by the teeth of one wheel, while the teeth of the other wheel are used for locking and frictional rest. The pallets are cut through the balance-staff.
Signed 'Bompard A Paris'.
Diam 48mm

526 Jean Baptiste François Cronier
France Late 18th century
Movement only. Double virgule escapement. Oil sinks.
Signed 'Cronier A Paris No. 692'.
Diam 61mm
See page 73
Presented by Francis B. Adams, 1869

527 Le Paute fils France
Early 19th century
Gold case. White enamel dial with subsidiary seconds dial. Steel loop hands. Fusee. Plain balance. Robin escapement. Repeater.
Signed 'M. Le Paute fils Paris 4904'.
This is probably Pierre Michel Le Paute who died 1849.
Gold chain and key attached.
Diam 53mm
Presented by Sir David Salomons Bt, 1924

528 John Ham England
Early 19th century
Movement only. White enamel dial. Subsidiary seconds dial. Gold spade hands. Smith's five-tooth lever escapement, see number 533. Signed 'John Ham Skinner Street London 62479. Patentee'.
Diam 47mm
Nelthropp Collection

529 James Gregory [England] c1800
Movement only. White enamel dial. Frictional rest escapement. A small brass verge-type wheel acts on two half-pallets on the balance-staff which is offset to one side of the escape-wheel. Bridge-cock. Steel balance. There is no mainspring barrel, the spring being contained by a fixed brass guard.
Signed 'James Gregory Ormskirk 61'. Possibly an imported movement.
Diam 45mm
Presented by Evan Roberts, 1893

530 James Houghton England c1800
Movement only. White enamel dial. Gold spade hands.
Frictional rest escapement. Two co-axial escape-wheels with ratchet teeth act on a single pallet on the balance-staff. Engraved cock. Plain steel balance. Mainspring missing. There is no mainspring barrel, the mainspring being contained by brass pegs fixed to the back plate. Signed 'Jas. Houghton Ormskirk No. 690'.
Diam 45mm

531 Anonymous France or Switzerland c1800
Silver engine-turned case. Flat band with engraved pattern. Engine-turned bezel. Stirrup pendant. Movement presses in. White enamel dial. Eccentric overlapping hour and seconds circles. Gold hands. Frictional rest escapement giving impulse only on alternate beats. The teeth of a small verge-type escape wheel rest on the circular face of the balance-staff before escaping through a curved slot cut out from the staff, giving impulse as it passes. The very large balance and circular cock cover the whole of the top plate. The cock is pierced with the initials AMD and a dolphin. There are two going barrels.
Diam 56mm
Nelthropp Collection

532 Joshua Ryland England c1810
Movement only. White enamel dial. Frictional rest escapement. Two co-axial escape-wheels have staggered, ratchet-shaped teeth which act on a single pallet on the balance-staff. Engraved cock. Fusee and barrel. Signed 'Josh. Ryland Ormskirk No 344'.
For a similar escapement by James Ryland, presumably father of Joshua, see number 519.
Diam 47mm
Presented by Evan Roberts, 1893

533 Thomas Smith   England
HM 1812
Silver pair-case. Stamped WR.
Enamel dial. Gold centre seconds hand.
Subsidiary dial for hours and minutes.
Signed 'Smith Coventry'.
The escapement is a type of rack lever
known as the 'Smith five-tooth lever'.
The escape wheel has five long pointed
teeth acting on the chamfered faces of a
lever whose arbor is at right angles to the
escape-wheel arbor. The lever has a
segmental rack of teeth geared to a pinion
on the balance-staff to which it imparts a
pirouette action, beating seconds. Flat
brass balance-wheel with three brass
poising screws. Solid cock engraved with
Royal Arms on table and PATENT on foot.
Signed 'Thoˢ Smith, Coventry Nº 25'.
Samuel Smith of Coventry took out a
patent for this escapement, 3620, on
December 9th 1812.
Diams 58 and 50mm
See also numbers 528, 534 and page 73
Presented by A.C. Meader

534 Robert Payne   England
HM 1813
Silver case; originally pair-case, outer
missing.
White enamel dial inscribed 'Patent'.
Centre seconds. Subsidiary dial for hours
and minutes.
The escapement is a type of rack lever
known as the 'Smith five-tooth lever
escapement' described in catalogue
number 533 immediately above qv.
Presumably Payne used the escapement
under licence from Smith. No jewelling
apart from diamond endstone to balance-
staff. Fusee. Solid balance-cock, the table
engraved with a serpent; the foot
engraved PATENT.
Signed 'Robt. Payne Walthamstow.
No. 144'.
Diam 51mm
Nelthropp Collection

535 Du Bois & Fils   France   c1825
Movement only. Silver engine-turned
dial. Sunk hour circle above centre.
Open sector shows bob on balance against
blued back below centre. Centre seconds
with narrow seconds ring.
Frictional rest escapement which is a
variant of Paul Garnier's.
Two very small steel escape-wheels, each
have four staggered curved teeth which
act on a disc having a vee-shaped notch of
125°, the edges of which alternately
receive impulse. This disc is on an arbor on
which also is mounted a wheel of 18 teeth
engaging with a pinion of 6 teeth on the
balance-staff, imparting to it a pirouette

action, beating seconds. Signed 'Du Bois
et Fils' (Paris) but as the dial is stamped
'P.G. 1281' the movement may have been
supplied by Paul Garnier to Du Bois.
The watch was purchased in Hanover by
George IV and given to Mr Walker, his
apothecary.
Diam 50mm
See Charles Gros, *Echappement D' Horloges
et de Montres*, (1913), fig 110
Presented by B.L. Vulliamy, 1849

536 Anonymous   [Switzerland]
c1840
Movement only. Enamel dial.
Quarter repeater. Virgule escapement.
Diam 54mm
Collinson Collection

537 James Ferguson Cole   England
HM 1847–8
Gold case.
White enamel dial. Subsidiary seconds
dial. Steel fleurs-de-lys hands.
A rotating detent placed between the
escape wheel and the balance-staff serves
both to unlock the escape-wheel and
impart impulse to the balance.
Compensation balance. Spiral balance-
spring with overcoil. Signed 'J.F. Cole
Invᵗ London No 1848'.
Diam 55mm
See Clutton & Daniels, *Watches*, p 123
and figs 66–7 and 551–2.
Nelthropp Collection

538 Anonymous   France or
Switzerland   c1850
Movement only. Enamel dial.
Virgule escapement in an unusually thin
movement having an elaborately engraved
full back plate.
Diam 48mm
Bequeathed by T. Vickery, 1946

539 Bulova   America   1969
Steel wristwatch case.
Skeletonised dial.
Bulova-Accutron electronic tuning-fork
movement.
The tuning-fork makes 360 vibrations a
second, energised by a small mercury
battery and electro-magnetic circuit. The
battery life is 12 months.
Together with this watch is shown some of
the fine-gauge copper wire used in the
circuit. Each watch contains 250 yards of
insulated wire ·02mm (about $\frac{1}{1200}$in) thick.
See page 73
Diam 36mm
Presented by the Bulova Watch Company
of USA, 1970

537a

537b

539

Clocks

Pendulum clocks

552a

Four of the early pendulum clocks, numbers 540, 541, 542 and 558, belong strictly to the important class of pre-pendulum balance-wheel clocks, having been converted to pendulum some time after its introduction. In order that they may be judged in their true chronological sequence they have been entered twice, once in this section with a brief description and the other with a full description in the section dealing with balance-wheel clocks.

No doubt it is because of storage problems that the Collection has not acquired more long-case pendulum clocks, but of those it has, some are of great interest. Catalogue number 543 (illustrated) is one of Tompion's earliest clocks, and has a short pendulum. Catalogue number 544 is an early example of East's pendulum clocks, although much restored and in a fine but not original case. But without question it is the group comprising numbers 551, 552 and 553 (all three are illustrated), the work of John and James Harrison, that is among the Collection's most important and rare possessions. These two brothers, carpenters of Barrow-on-Humber, at first together and finally John alone, are well known for their invention of a timekeeper which would perform sufficiently accurately in a ship at sea to enable its longitude to be determined. Because of their training their earliest work was made almost entirely of oak. Also, because the oils then available had such a detrimental effect on the timekeeping of clocks and watches, they did everything possible to avoid its use and eliminate friction generally. They finally produced clocks in which the brass pivots ran in bushes of lignum vitae, a wood with a naturally greasy surface, and thus the use of oil was eliminated. Similarly, the bearings of the peculiar but elegant grasshopper escapement employed glass and gold while the pallets were of wood. Catalogue number 551 is Harrison's earliest clock movement; it has an ordinary anchor escapement and is dated 1713. Number 552 is only basically a John and James Harrison movement of c1726–8 of little known provenance which had survived in a more or less fragmentary state. It has recently been restored by the Company with great care using the basically similar James Harrison clock, number 553, as a copy for all replaced wheelwork, as well as the grasshopper escapement, adjustable cycloid cheeks and gridiron pendulum. Most important of the Harrison clocks is catalogue number 553, a complete clock by James Harrison in a black ebonised case which was acquired by the Clockmakers' Company almost a hundred years ago. This immensely rare and important clock is illustrated in colour.

Turning to spring-driven pendulum clocks of the table or mantel variety, catalogue number 559, by Samuel Knibb, is characteristic of the first decade of the pendulum and number 565, by Pieter Visbach (illustrated), is typical of the first Dutch pendulum clocks, with Huygens' cycloidal cheeks to overcome circular error. The clock had survived in a very bad state, which makes it difficult to date although it is probably a good deal earlier than the one provisionally ascribed to it in the catalogue.

One of the finest of all the table pendulum clocks is catalogue number 564 (illustrated), the complicated astronomical clock by Samuel Watson, which may have belonged to Sir Isaac Newton.

The Collection's important group of watches by John Grant is completed by his very fine long-case regulator clock, catalogue number 569, which is characteristically full of unusual features. It has Ellicott's type of compensation pendulum, a gravity escapement and goes for a month. It is very difficult to understand why, in a long-case clock with ample drop for a month-going weight, Grant should have decided to drive it by a spring. It was evidently made for his own use as it remained in the Grant family until presented to the Clockmakers' Company in 1883.

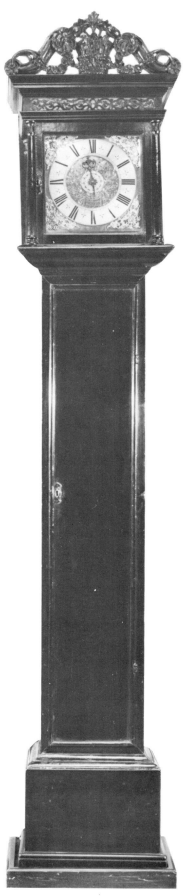

543

Weight-driven pendulum clocks

540 c1630 Lantern clock by **Peter Closon,** converted from balance to pendulum.
See Weight-driven balance-wheel clocks, page 91, and number 574 for a full description.
Presented by Victor Wilkins

541 Lantern clocks by **Jeffry Baylie,** third quarter seventeenth century, converted from balance to pendulum.
See Weight-driven balance-wheel clocks, page 92, and number 575 for a full description.

542 Lantern clock by **Thomas Loomes,** third quarter seventeenth century. Converted from balance to pendulum.
See Weight-driven balance-wheel clocks, page 92, and number 576 for a full description.

543 Long-case clock, striking and alarm
Thomas Tompion England c1672
Ebonised pinewood case with cresting on top.
Brass 10in dial with silvered hour circle and alarm disc. Cherub spandrels. Centre engraved with floral design. One hand.
30-hour movement of the posted lantern type. Verge escapement and short pendulum. Number 151 is stamped on one pillar but this does not tie up with Tompion's system of numbering which he did not start until c1680. Alarm mechanism missing. Signed 'Tho. Tompion Londini fecit'.
Tompion was born 1639, a Freeman of the Clockmakers' Company 1671, Master 1704, died 1713.
See page 77
See also R.W. Symonds, *Thomas Tompion,* page 276 and fig 95.
Presented by William Wing, 1879

544 Long-case clock, striking
Edward East England c1675
Marquetry case. Rising hood with twisted columns. Round window in door.
Height 6ft 4in. The case is not original to this movement and has been cut down to accommodate the 9¼in dial.
Dial plate 9¼in. Narrow silvered hour circle with minute figures at every 5. Engraved spandrels.
8-day movement. Anchor escapement. Bolt and shutter maintaining power. Signed 'Edwardus East Londini'.
The striking train is original but the going

train from the centre pinion upwards had been replaced in the nineteenth century.
See also page 77
Presented by Executors of T.F. Mallett, 1947
See also colour plate V

545 Clock movement, striking
Joseph Knibb England c1685
Gilt 10in dial with engraved spandrels. 30-hour movement. Original anchor escapement and long pendulum.
Signed 'Joseph Knibb. Londini'.
Presented by P.G. Osborne

546 Long-case clock movement, striking
Thomas Tompion England c1700
Brass 12in dial with silvered hour circle and seconds dial, the latter inside the hour circle at VI. Cherub spandrels. Bolt and shutter maintaining power.
4-month inverted train, the escape-wheel being at the bottom with the anchor below it. Latched back plate.
Signed 'Tho. Tompion'.
Presented by Saul Isaac, 1887

547 Miniature lantern clock, alarm
George Graham England
Early 18th century
Small clock with arched dial plate, 4·7in × 3·2in. One hand. Engraved spandrels. Verge escapement with short pendulum. Alarm (bell missing).
Signed 'Geo. Graham London'.
Presented by Executors of Mrs E.N. Noble Jones, 1947

548 Long-case clock, striking
George Stratford England
Early 18th century
Marquetry case with round window in door. Flat top. Ebonised columns.
Height 7ft 1in.
Brass 12in dial with silvered hour circle and seconds dial. Matt centre. Day of month aperture. Crown and angel spandrels. Steel pierced hands. Month movement. Anchor escapement.
Signed 'Geo Stratford London'.
Stratford was a Freeman of the Clockmakers' Company in 1704.

549 Small turret clock movement
Langley Bradley England 1701-2
The movement is 10in × 11in and is similar to a long-case movement with anchor escapement and seconds pendulum. It was in the Greycoat School,

Westminster. Signed 'Langley Bradley
London 1701/2'.
Bradley was a Freeman of the Clockmakers'
Company in 1695, Master 1726.
Presented by the Governors of the
Greycoat School, 1905

550 Long-case clock, striking
John May   England   c1705
Walnut case with round window in door.
Flat top with ormolu band below. Brass
12in dial with silvered hour circle and
seconds dial. Matt centre. Crown and
angel spandrels. Steel pierced hands.
Month movement. Anchor escapement.
Signed 'John May London'.
May was of Dutch origin and was a
Freeman of the Clockmakers' Company in
1692, died 1738.
Presented by Mrs May, 1922

551 Long-case clock movement
John Harrison   England   1713
Oak dial with aperture for seconds.
Silvered chapter ring.
8-day movement. Strikes hours. Anchor
escapement. Wheels of wood.
The clock is wound by removing the lower
spandrels and inserting a key with end
teeth. The winder of this clock, although
old, may not be original. This is the
earliest known clock by John Harrison
completed when he was 20 and living at
Barrow-on-Humber. Similar clock
movements are in the Science Museum
(1715) and Nostell Priory (1717).
Signed 'Jᵒn Harrison 1713' on the
calendar wheel and also in another hand
'S.B. 1803' – presumably a repair date.
See page 77
See also H. Quill, *John Harrison, The Man
who found Longitude*, fig 2 and 3

552 Long-case clock movement, striking
[John & James Harrison]   England
1726–8
For many years this 8-day striking
movement has been exhibited in an
incorrect case and fitted with a
comparatively modern anchor
escapement, wooden pendulum and metal
rack striking. These parts were discarded
when the movement was rebuilt by the
Company in 1970–1 with a Harrison
grasshopper escapement, gridiron
pendulum and Harrison's type of striking
mechanism, all copied exactly from the
Company's other basically similar
Harrison clock, catalogue number 553. All
the oak used in this construction was of
contemporary date and came from
Barrow-on-Humber where the Harrisons
originally built the clock.

551

552b

79

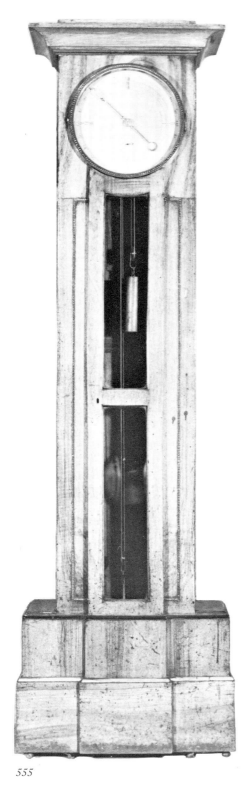

555

See page 77
See full report by Colonel Quill in the
Company's library.
Presented by W. Thoms, 1875

553 Long-case clock, striking, calendar
James Harrison England 1728
Black ebonised case. Height 7ft 4ins.
Equation of time table in John Harrison's
handwriting behind glass in door, and is
corrected for the change to the Gregorian
Calendar in 1752.
Painted wooden dial with 11in silvered
hour circle. Seconds and day of month
show through apertures.
8-day movement. Plates and wheels of oak.
Roller lantern pinions of lignum vitae and
brass. Grasshopper escapement. Gridiron
pendulum. Brass adjustable cycloid
cheeks. Maintaining power.
Signed 'Barrow James Harrison' in arch of
dial and 'James Harrison 3rd 1728 Barrow'
on calendar wheel. James Harrison (1704–
66) was the younger brother of John
(1693–1776). The clock passed from John
Harrison's descendants to Sir John Barton
of the Mint where it remained until 1869.
It was then bought by R. Napier of
Gairloch and on his death in 1877 it was
acquired by the Company. The clock was
put in going order in 1966.
See page 77
See also H. Quill, *John Harrison and the
Man who found Longitude*, pp 24–8 and
figs 7 and 9–12
See also colour plate V

554 Long-case clock, striking
George Graham England c1750
Oak case 6ft 10in high.
12in dial. Seconds dial. Spandrel
ornaments.
8-day striking movement. Dead-beat
escapement. Bolt and shutter maintaining
power. Iron pendulum. Signed on dial
'Geo. Graham London' and numbered
779.
Bequeathed by Frank Mercer, 1970

555 Long-case clock
Anonymous [Continental] c1775
Teak case with ormolu mounts.
Dial 11in silvered. A central steel hand,
turning in four hours, shows minutes on
an outer circle, with each quadrant
divided 1–60. The hand carries a movable
arrowhead pointing to hours engraved at
the quarters of three concentric circles;
the arrowhead, on completion of a
revolution of the hand, flirts to the next
circle, returning at 12 to the innermost.
Benjamin Franklin, the celebrated

politician and scientist of Philadelphia,
USA, 1706–90, made clocks with three
wheels and two pinions and this
arrangement of dial.
Nelthropp Collection

556 Long-case clock
Thomas Vickery England 1931
Pollarded oak case made by Thomas
Vickery.
The dial gives equation of time; times of
sunrise and sunset; perpetual calendar;
age and phases of the moon; position of
principal constellations; sun's place in the
ecliptic.
The escapement is dead-beat with seconds
pendulum with Invar rod.
It chimes the Westminster or
Whittington quarters alternately and also
strikes the hours from one train. It also
plays a tune every 3 hours. There is a
different tune for each day of the week,
changed automatically at midnight.
Signed 'T. Vickery Bridgnorth AD 1931
Invit et Fecit'
See *Country Life*, January 8th 1946,
pp 116–17; *Horological Journal*, January
1946, p 22. See also number 557.
Bequeathed by Thomas Vickery of
Bridgnorth, 1946

557 Also, parts of a second perpetual
calendar and astronomical clock under
construction by Mr Vickery at the time of
his death in 1946.

Spring-driven pendulum clocks

558 Small chamber clock with steel case
Anonymous Late 16th century
Converted from balance to short
pendulum.
See Spring driven balance-wheel clocks,
page 94, and number 583 for a full
description.
Nelthropp Collection

559 Table clock, striking
Samuel Knibb England c1665
Ebony veneered case with no metal
mounts. Pediment top.
9¼in dial, engraved with lilies, tulips, etc.
Two steel hands.
8-day fusee movement. Verge escapement
and short pendulum. Hour and ½-hour
striking with hammers located in an
extension above the movement.
Count-wheel overlaps the back plate. All
pillars are latched to back plate.

559ᵃ

Back plate is plain except for engraving on
count-wheel, pendulum cock and
hammer arbor plate. Signed on back plate
only 'Samuel Knibb Londini fecit'.
Samuel Knibb was a Freeman of the
Clockmakers' Company 1663, died 1674.
See also page 77
For illustrations and description see '*The
First twelve years of the English Pendulum
Clock*', Exhibition Catalogue 1969
by Ronald Lee. Exhibit 20.
Presented by Norman Shaw, 1950

559ᵇ

561a

561b

560 Table clock, striking and repeating
Christopher Gould England c1700
Ebonised case with ormolu mounts on
basket top.
Dial 6in, gilt, with silvered chapter ring
and cherub spandrels. Lever at top of dial
with '*suona*' and '*Non suona*'. Two steel
hands.
8-day movement. Verge escapement.
Short pendulum. Fusees. Pull repeating.
Signed 'Chr. Gould Londini'.
Gould was a Freeman of the Clockmakers'
Company 1682, died 1718.

561 Table clock, striking
Henry Jones England c1675
Walnut case with lifting handle.
Dial gilt with silvered chapter ring and
cherub spandrels.
Calendar aperture. Steel hands.
8-day movement. Verge escapement.
Latched plates.
Fusee with gut. Locking plate striking,
hours only. Signed 'Henry Jones in ye
Temple'.
Jones was a Freeman of the Clockmakers'
Company 1663, Master 1691, died 1695.

562 Table clock, striking and repeating
Thomas Tompion England c1700
Ebonised case with ormolu mounts,
basket top. Dial gilt with silvered chapter
ring.
Apertures for mock pendulum and
calendar.
Subsidiary dials for regulation and strike/
silent in upper corners. Steel hands.
8-day movement. Latched plates. Verge
escapement. Pull quarter-hour repeating
on one bell. Signed 'Thomas Tompion
Londini Fecit'.
Tompion was born 1639, a Freeman of the
Clockmakers' Company 1671, Master
1703–4, died 1713.

563 Table clock, striking and repeating
Richard Baker England
Late 17th century
Kingwood veneered case with ormolu
mounts and basket top.
Dial 7in gilt. Silvered hour circle and day
of month aperture. Cherub spandrels.
Steel hands.
8-day movement. Verge escapement and
short pendulum. Tulip engraved back
plate. Pierced engraved pendulum cock.
Fusees and gut. Pull repeating with three
bells. Signed 'Richd. Baker London'.
Baker was a Freeman of the Clockmakers'
Company 1685, died 1710.

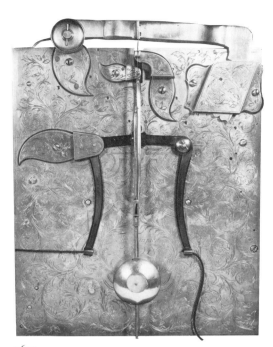

562a

562b

563a

563b

564 Table clock, astronomical
Samuel Watson England
Late 17th century
Ebonised case with gilt statuette of
Mercury above. Spigoted to turn on a
modern fixed base. Square 11in dial with
cherub spandrels.
The fixed outermost ring on the dial gives
the times of sunrise and sunset, this being
denoted by a gilt image of the sun which
revolves clockwise once in 365 days. The
moving ring to which the sun is fixed is
engraved with the months of the year and
corresponding signs of the Zodiac. Thus,
the sun is shown fixed in the Zodiac
according to the geocentric Ptolemaic
belief. Next is a silvered chapter ring on
which the hours and minutes are indicated
by a single hand. The brass lunar dial
within this chapter ring revolves once in
$29\frac{1}{2}$ days and has an aperture showing the
phases of the moon. Also engraved on this
dial are the lines for trine, quadrature,
sextile and opposition of the moon used in
making astrological deductions. The
innermost set of seven rings shows the time
of the setting of the moon during the first
half of its lunation and that of its rising
during the second half, each ring
referring to different months.
8-day movement. Anchor escapement.
Half seconds pendulum with separate
sliding weight for regulation. Engraved
back plate. Rack-striking.
Signed 'Sam Watson Londini Fecit'.
See page 77; also *Horological Journal*,
December 1948, pp 750–9 and *The
Clockwork of the Heavens*, Exhibition
Catalogue 1973, compiled by Asprey & Co,
Exhibit 31, who also gave the annotated
drawing of the dial.
Watson was a Freeman of the Clockmakers'
Company in 1692 and was 'Mathematician
in Ordinary to His Majesty'. There is a
strong tradition that this clock belonged to
Sir Isaac Newton.
Presented by H.J. Adams, 1882.

564a

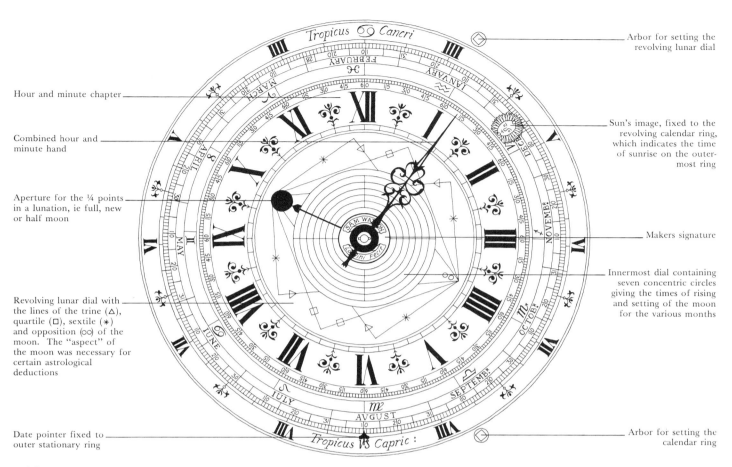

Arbor for setting the revolving lunar dial

Hour and minute chapter

Combined hour and minute hand

Aperture for the ¼ points in a lunation, ie full, new or half moon

Sun's image, fixed to the revolving calendar ring, which indicates the time of sunrise on the outermost ring

Makers signature

Innermost dial containing seven concentric circles giving the times of rising and setting of the moon for the various months

Revolving lunar dial with the lines of the trine (△), quartile (□), sextile (✳) and opposition (☍) of the moon. The "aspect" of the moon was necessary for certain astrological deductions

Date pointer fixed to outer stationary ring

Arbor for setting the calendar ring

564b

564c

565 Table clock, striking
Pieter Visbach Holland c1700
Ebonised case. Dial 9in × 7in hinged to
the case and carrying the movement,
4in × 3in attached to it.
Brass dial covered with crimson velvet
(restoration) and with gilt hinged
escutcheon. Silver hour ring with
minute band with every minute marked.
The gilt hands, in correct style, are
modern.
8-day movement. Verge escapement.
Pendulum with silk suspension and
cycloidal cheeks. A single-going barrel for
going and striking trains. Signed 'Pieter
Visbach Fecit Hagae met priuilege'. The
'privilege' refers to Huygens' patent for
the cycloidal cheeks.
This clock is difficult to date and 1700 is a
conservative estimate. It could well be
considerably earlier.
See also page 77
Presented by Daniel Clarke, 1895

566 Table clock, striking
John Ellicott England c1750
Ebonised case.
Silvered 7in dial. Pierced steel hands.
Verge escapement. Fusees.
Signed 'Ellicott London'.

567 Orrery clock [French]
Late 18th century
Consists of a glass globe 65cms diameter
supported by three bronze Herculean
figures and enclosing a small timepiece
with anchor escapement and pendulum
with silk suspension. This timepiece has an
enamelled chapter ring showing the clock
mechanism through the centre.
Gilt fleur-de-lys hands.
A revolving orrery surmounts the clock
and the surrounding glass dome is
engraved with various constellations.
Purchased by the Company, 1879.

568 Table clock movement
Grignion & Son England
Late 18th century
Silvered 11in dial with sunk seconds dial.
Steel hands.
Dead-beat escapement giving impulse on
alternate swings, one pallet giving
impulse and the other locking only.
Maintaining power.
Signed 'Grignion & Son London'.
The firm was composed of Daniel, born
1684, died 1763; and Thomas, born 1713,
died 1784.
Presented by John Grant, 1875

565a

565b

569a

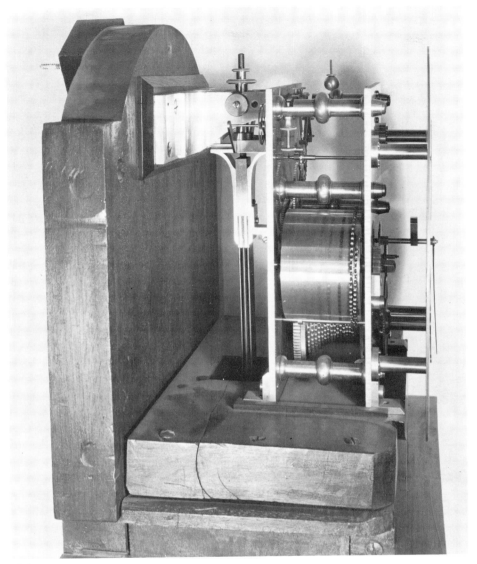

569b

569 Long-case clock
John Grant England c1800
Mahogany case with glass door and round glass panels at the sides of the hood.
Height 6ft 4in.
Silvered 12in dial with central minute hand and subsidiary dials for hours and minutes.
Gravity escapement. Seconds pendulum with Ellicott's brass and steel compensation. The month movement is spring driven. Signed 'John Grant Fleet Street London no.185'.
John Grant was a Freeman of the Clockmakers' Company 1781, Warden and died 1810.
See page 77
Presented by Miss Troughton, niece of Grant's son, 1883

570 Skeleton clock
Anonymous England
Mid 19th century
Silvered skeleton dial with subsidiary seconds dial.
Pin-wheel escapement. Brass pendulum with suspension spring. Two going barrels.
8-day movement. Count-wheel hour striking.
Glass dome on circular rosewood base, 400mm high.
Presented by John Byram, 1963

571 Spherical skeleton clock
H. Gratte England c1800
The spherical skeleton movement is supported on a brass pillar provided with

three folding legs. Height 270mm. Verge escapement, fusee, pendulum and hour striking on a bell. The time is shown in hours and minutes by means of two revolving bands which are read against a fixed red glass sun, the minutes being indicated on the upper band and hours on the lower. The horizontal dial is calibrated in four sections of 0° to 90° and the cardinal points N, S, E, and W are also shown but the use of this is not clear. Signed 'Henricus Gratte, invenit & fecit Londini'.
See also *Horological Journal*, February 1951, p 94; *Antiquarian Horology*, December 1957, p iii.
Presented by Lady Spencer-Jones, 1961

Balance-wheel clocks

This category covers almost five centuries, from the most erratic to the most precise achievements in timekeeping, the latter being represented by Marine timekeepers. These have been grouped under their own heading.

Iron Gothic clocks are difficult to date, but catalogue numbers 572 and 573 are typical of the late fifteenth century. Apart from these there is one steel sixteenth-century clock (number 583) and three lantern clocks of the second and third quarters of the seventeenth century (numbers 574, 575 and 576) which started life with balance-wheel escapements and were subsequently converted to pendulum.

The unsprung balance-wheel escapement had a late survival in Japan, and the Collection has three eighteenth- and nineteenth-century examples (catalogue numbers 578, 579 and 580). Of these, number 580 has the double escapement unique to the Japanese system of time-recording prior to 1870, in which the night and day had each an equal number of hours of varying duration according to the season. The day and nighttime escapements automatically gave way to each other in turn, but needed constant regulation by the foliot weights as the seasons changed.

Spring-driven balance clocks for the most part, naturally, are portable, but the Collection has one of the greatest splendour which is too large to be moved at all easily. This is the astronomical and automata standing clock of about 1625 by Johann Schneider, which is illustrated in colour (catalogue number 585) and fully described under its catalogue entry. Standing 32in high it is typical of the large, complicated and decorative metal domestic clocks which were fashionable in the fifty years before the pendulum.

Such clocks however are exceptional and probably none was made in England. However, native clocks of the first half of the seventeenth century are none the less pleasing for their small size and restraint, as may be judged from the exquisite table clock only $3\frac{1}{2}$in high by Henry Archer (catalogue number 584, illustrated). The two views of the movement show also the fine technical mastery which the British masters had achieved by this date (about 1625) which was to carry them to world supremacy by the end of the century. The engraved border to the top plate and the pegged and pinned balance-cock are all characteristic features.

Many table clocks of the early sixteenth century are so small that it is difficult to decide whether they should be described as clocks or watches and this applies to the two little German drum clocks (catalogue numbers 581 and 582) certainly no later than 1550, as has already been remarked in the introduction to verge watches. Catalogue number 581 is illustrated.

Throughout most of the seventeenth and eighteenth centuries travelling clocks in the form of very large watches, 4 or 5in in diameter, were popular and were the object of much refined decoration. Before about 1690 they had alarm and striking trains, and afterwards alarm and repeating. The cases therefore had to be pierced, and this gave the opportunity for exquisite pierced and engraved cases of which examples in the Collection are French clocks of the mid seventeenth century, catalogue numbers 587 and 588. None excelled Edward East for elegance and excellence in this field, but unfortunately the only example in the Collection is a movement only, but a superb one at that (catalogue number 586).

Marine timekeepers

We come at last to that section of the Collection in which it is perhaps richest of all, for in its marine timekeepers it possesses several unique or immensely rare pieces.

Christiaan Huygens had been the first to attempt a marine timekeeper and indeed, all his horological work had that end in view; but he never came within measurable distance of success.

The eventual solution to the problem was to be found in a detached escapement, an isochronous balance-spring and a compensated balance. Henry Sully (1680–1728) lived too early to make use of these developments, and although the spiral balance-spring existed in his time he evidently realised that its instability under temperature changes made it unsuitable for a precision marine timekeeper. He therefore attempted to design a timekeeper utilising a balance working in conjunction with a horizontal pivoted pendulum. To this he added a correction for circular error and a perfectly sound form of frictional rest escapement, and hoped that the resulting timekeeper would perform with the necessary degree of accuracy. Although it could now be predicted that such a machine would not succeed, Sully was at any rate the first person to tackle the problem scientifically, and the possession of an example made almost certainly in 1724 (it is not known if any other has survived) is a matter of the greatest interest (catalogue number 597, illustrated).

Another thirty-five years were to elapse before John Harrison produced his successful H4 (as it is now always known, it being the fourth marine timekeeper to be constructed by him). Its predecessors, the three huge and exquisite machines now at the National Maritime Museum, Greenwich, were very complicated, extremely expensive to make and difficult to transport, and so John Harrison decided, some time after 1750, to experiment with the construction of smaller and cheaper timekeepers in the form of watches. The long, moving and exciting story of how this lone ex-village carpenter overcame the mechanical difficulties that had baffled the best brains of his day, thus qualifying for the rich prize of £20,000 offered by Parliament, and then had to overcome even greater legal obstacles to get the money, is well known. Equally well known is that even when his large watch H4 performed with great precision on two official sea-going trials to the West Indies, he was still required to make a duplicate in order to prove that the accuracy of the first was not a fluke. It is this final timekeeper, H5 as it is known the world over, but 'No 2' as he engraved on it, which the Collection owns. The catalogue number is 598 and it is illustrated in colour. It is certainly the proudest possession of the Clockmakers' Company.

An important factor in the success of Harrison's H4 and H5 was a remontoir re-wound every $7\frac{1}{2}$ seconds, and by the attempts of the experimentors who followed him attempts were made to carry the remontoir into the escapement itself, in which form it is known as a constant-force escapement. The first person to do this was Thomas Mudge, but he was unable to control the almost insoluble problems of temperature compensation which the escapement produced; despite which he did succeed in securing a rate which was not surpassed for many years. He himself completed three of these timekeepers of the utmost beauty and superb finish; after which his son set up a team of craftsmen to make them. But the venture was not successful and although about fifteen were completed, most of them were subsequently converted to a more conventional escapement. The example in the Collection (catalogue number 606, illustrated) is one of the 36-hour models and is, fortunately, in perfect and original condition.

Josiah Emery tackled the problem along similar, but sounder, lines with the added advantage of a compensation balance as opposed to Mudge's compensation curb. It is not known how many he made, but only his No 1 is known to have survived and is number 602 in the Collection (illustrated). It is a most beautiful and superbly executed mechanism and, although it was not successful, this was probably due more than anything else to the inadequacy of the compensation balance which was a copy of Arnold's 's' balance.

But all such complicated tours de force had been out of date for a good fifteen years before they were made, by virtue of the simple and robust detent escapement marine timekeepers which John Arnold had been producing in a successful and reliable form since about 1776. Two of his earliest experiments, owned by the Royal Society, were anything but successful, and it was only with his development of the detent passing-spring; the helical balance-spring; and probably his third form of compensation balance that he arrived at a marine timekeeper which was acceptably reliable, cheap and accurate. Owing to the custom of bringing his watches and chronometers back to Arnold for modernisation, unaltered early examples scarcely exist and although among the many Arnolds in the Collection are No 1, of about 1771 (catalogue number 599) and No 14 (number 600) both have been substantially modernised by Arnold at various subsequent dates.

The two brothers Brockbanks produced early on a variant of the spring detent escapement, designed for them by one of their employees named Peto, which possessed the theoretical advantage of combining the good points of Arnold's and Earnshaw's models while avoiding their disadvantages. Examples are quite rare and catalogue number 601 is an early specimen, dating from about 1785.

Catalogue number 607 is a curious example of the work of George Margetts. Although he delighted in making very complicated astronomical trains, his going trains were usually not of an outstandingly high quality. This one has what is probably an unique feature in that the endstone taking the weight of the balance-staff is an agate disc, mounted on a platform geared to the great wheel, so as to revolve once in 5 hours. The clock also goes for 8 days. But its most curious feature is that there is no visible signature on the dial or movement except that in a strong light the ghost of the signature 'Margetts' may be read on the dial. In any case, the workmanship is all characteristic of him.

From 1800 onwards it would be tedious to describe in detail all the variants, of compensation balances in particular, that are to be found in the very large number of important marine chronometers to be found in the Collection. They are all described under their catalogue entries. Some of their wooden box-lids were removed many years ago for ease of display and nearly all of these disappeared during the last war.

No one, however, can fail to observe the enormous machine of about 1830 by Joseph Croucher (catalogue number 619, illustrated) employing Ulrich's constant-force escapement; an appliance which, for misapplied ingenuity and fruitless complication could hardly be surpassed. Lt-Commander Gould in his great work *The Marine Chronometer* remarked 'There is a quality of suspended animation about it suggestive of catalepsy'.

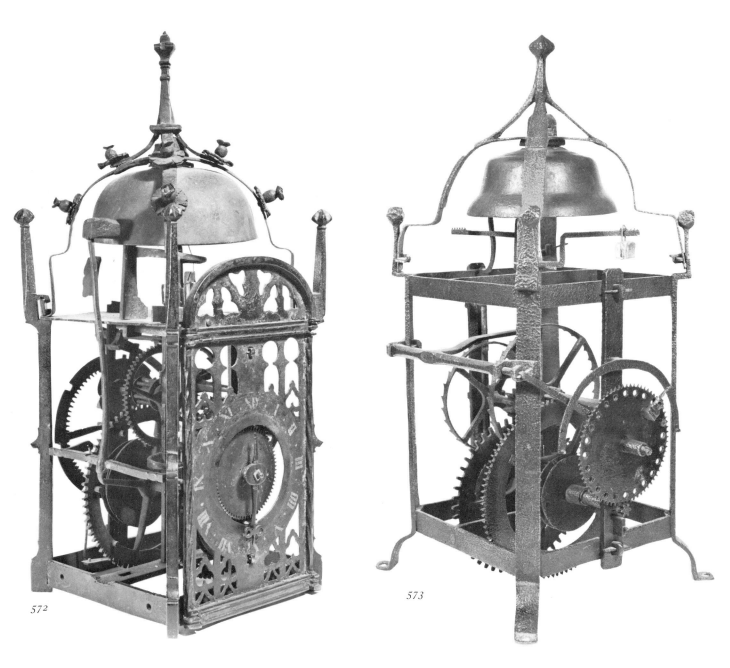

572

573

Weight-driven balance-wheel clocks

572 Wall clock
Anonymous [Germany]
15th century
Iron frame of four corner uprights
surmounted by four curved corner bars
forming a canopy supporting a bell. The
corner posts carry rosettes. The front has a
pierced iron plate on which hour figures
are painted. Striking mechanism without
warning. Verge escapement and bar foliot
with adjustable weights. Weight-driven.
Height 15in to top of bell.
Presented by W.E. Miller, 1934

573 Wall clock
Anonymous [Germany]
15th century
Iron frame of four corner uprights
surmounted by four curved corner bars
forming a canopy supporting the bell. All
detachable parts are fixed by wedges. Dial
wheel with 24 holes and pointer. A plate
with two pins is probably a support for a
ring hour circle. An alarm is set by
inserting a pin in one of the 24 holes which
tripped a detent. Bar foliot with
adjustable weights. Weight driven.
Height 20in to top of bell.

574 Lantern clock, striking
Peter Closon England c1630
The clock, originally with verge and
balance-wheel escapement, has been
converted to anchor and long pendulum.
Dial engraved with tulips. Steel hand.
Height to top of bell 16in. Signed 'Peter
Closon Neere Holburn Londini fecit'.
Peter Closon subscribed £5 in 1630
towards the cost of obtaining the Charter
of the Company. He held the office of
Senior Warden from 1636–9.
See also number 540 and page 78
Presented by Victor Wilkins

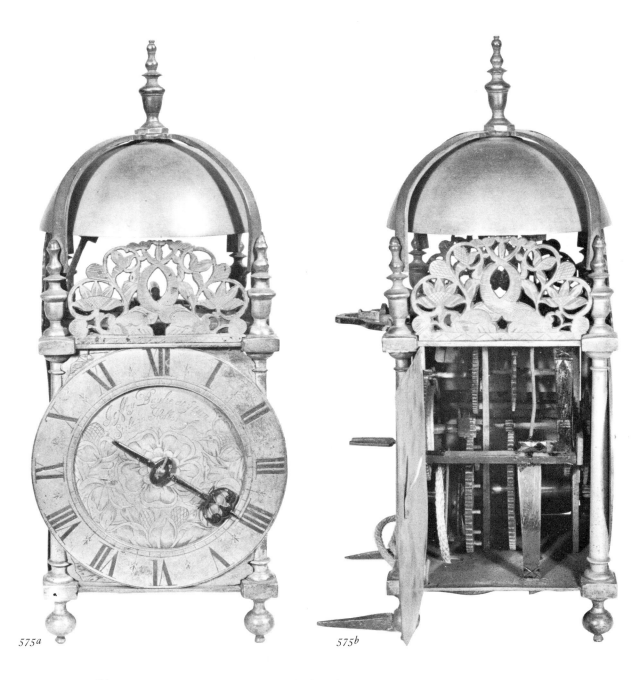

575*a*   575*b*

575 Lantern clock, striking
Jeffry Baylie England
Third quarter 17th century
Brass case with dolphin frets above.
6in dial engraved with tulips. Steel hand.
Verge and foliot escapement converted to
anchor and long pendulum. Height to top
of bell 13in. Signed 'Jeffry Baylie at ye
turn-Stile in Holburn fecit'.
Baylie was a Freeman of the Clockmakers'
Company 1646, Master 1674 and 1675.
See also number 541 and page 78

576 Lantern clock, striking
Thomas Loomes England
Third quarter 17th century
Brass case with floral frets above case. Top
finial missing. Dial 6in diameter engraved
with tulips. One hand. Weight driven.
Originally verge and balance-wheel
escapement converted to anchor and long
pendulum. Height 13in to the top of the
bell.
Signed 'Thomas Loomes at the Mermayd
In Lothbury'.
Loomes was a Freeman of the
Clockmakers' Company in 1649
See also number 542 and page 78

577 Miniature chamber clock
Anonymous Germany
Late 18th century
Gilt case 52mm high and 26mm wide
engraved with Germanic warriors on
sides and a view of a town in front.
Silver engraved dial. One hand.
Later weight-driven movement with verge
and balance. The clock is mounted on a
modern wooden bracket.
Presented by George Atkins, 1824

578 Japanese clock with automaton striking
Anonymous 18th century
Bronze case of rectangular form $8\frac{1}{2}$in high × $5\frac{1}{2}$in wide surmounted by an annular platform on four gilt pillars, with bell inside the platform. The whole is surmounted by a bronze seated figure holding a hammer for the bell. The sides and front plates are pierced bronze with turned corner pillars. Gilt dial on front plate with movable figure plates. Single hand.
Verge and foliot escapement. Weight driven.
The clock stands on a conical wooden stand of square plan section, 23in high.
Clock 15in high

579 Japanese clock
Anonymous 19th century
Rosewood case. Movement with foliot above a trunk constituting the dial. Time is indicated by a pointer attached to the weight with movable number plates.
Verge and foliot escapement. Height 50cm.
See also page
For Japanese clocks and timekeeping prior to 1873 see *Britten's Old Clocks and Watches* (7th or 8th editions), pp 250–5; also J. Drummond Robertson, *The Evolution of Clockwork*, pp 190–287.
Nelthropp Collection

580 Japanese clock
Anonymous c1850
This brass clock is 10in high and is of lantern-type driven by an endless cord and weight. It has double verge and foliot escapements. Both verge staffs are suspended by a thread and the change from day to night foliot takes place automatically, but the time of the day and night periods had to be varied according to the season by moving the foliot weights. The clock has striking, going and alarm mechanism and also has two calendar apertures. The train wheels are brass with steel arbors and pinions. The dial plate and also the back and sides are engraved with a floral design.
See also page 88
For Japanese clocks and timekeeping prior to 1873 see *Britten's Old Clocks and Watches* (7th or 8th editions), pp 250–5; also J. Drummond Robertson, *The Evolution of Clockwork*, pp 190–287.
Presented by Smiths Industries Ltd, 1968

Spring-driven balance-wheel clocks

581 Table clock
Anonymous Germany
Second quarter 16th century
Circular canister case, brass-gilt. Side engraved with three busts and intermediate foliage design. Cover engraved with the bust of a soldier with surrounding wreath.
Gilt dial with hour figures I–XII and

13–24 and central sun. Hand is replacement.
Verge and balance-wheel escapement. Three-wheel train. Long fusee. Ratchet set-up. Movement and plates all steel. Brass contrate and escape-wheels are replacements, and the original balance was probably of larger diameter. The back plate is stamped 'c'.
Diam 63mm Height 38mm
Nelthropp Collection

581a

581b

581c

583a

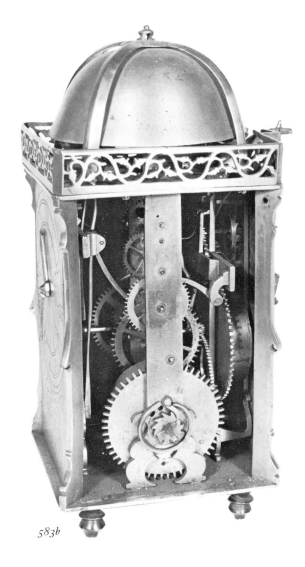

583b

582 Table clock
Anonymous Germany
Second quarter 16th century
Circular canister case, brass-gilt. Side
engraved with figures of three soldiers and
scrolled foliage. Cover is engraved with
foliage and the bust of a German lady and
date 1581. However, the '81' is crudely
engraved on a piece of ungilded metal let
into the cover and is clearly not original.
Gilt dial with hour figures I–XII and
13–24 with a central sun. Touch-pins.
Verge and balance escapement. Three-
wheel train. Long fusee. Ratchet set-up.
Bristle regulator. Movement and plates all
iron pinned together. Verge, balance and
bristles replaced in 1973.
Diam 68mm   Height 45mm
Nelthropp Collection

583 Chamber clock
Anonymous [Germany]
Late 16th century
Steel case. Four moulded corner uprights
set at an angle. Fixed dial plate; back and
side plates removable. Pierced steel
balustrade round the top. Four-arm
support for bell.
Hour circle engraved on plain steel plate
with central sun. Concentric plain steel
alarm-set ring. Steel arrow hand.
Spring driven. Originally verge and
balance escapement but replaced by brass
wheels and pendulum. Striking train in
steel and original. Alarm train at right
angles, also original.
Height to balustrade 150mm
Width 88mm
See also number 558 and page 88
Nelthropp Collection

584 Small table clock
Henry Archer England c1625
Circular canister case, brass-gilt, with
pierced dome top containing a bell,
surmounted by a horizontal dial with a
plain silver chapter ring. The centre of the
dial is gilt and engraved. Single steel hand.
The lower, drum-shaped portion of the
clock is engraved with hunting scenes and
contains two doors, one to inspect the
fusee and the other the striking train.
The pierced dome which covers the bell is
engraved with eight lion-like masks.
The case stands on three bun feet.
The movement is brass except for the
balance-wheel which is later and has had a
balance-spring and regulator added. Verge
escapement. Pinned-on cock of simple
s-shape design. Back plate has an
engraved border. Early type of long fusee

with a chain which is a replacement of the original gut. The striking train has a going barrel; the fly is missing.
Signed 'Henry Archer'.
The case of this clock was probably imported from France and, as it has two inspection doors, was intended to be fitted with a movement possessing two fusees, but Archer evidently decided on a going barrel for the strike side and no alarm.
Henry Archer was a 'Clockmaker Citizen' in London in 1622 and in that year signed with fifteen others a petition asking for protection against bad workmanship.
In 1632 his name appears in the Charter of the Clockmakers' Company as an original Warden and later that year he was appointed Deputy Master while the Master, David Ramsay, was out of the country.
Height 86mm   Diam 78mm
See also page 88
See also colour plate I

585 Astronomical and automaton standing clock
Johann Schneider   Germany   c1625
The clock is of gilt-metal throughout, consisting of an octagon base, cast and chiselled, supporting, by a group of boys and a dolphin, a cylindrical main clock.
This is surmounted by a small rectangular clock with a canopy on pillars above it.
Under the canopy is an automaton group of St George and the Dragon and above is a figure in Roman dress.
The dial of the main clock, starting from the outside, has a broad silver band on which a year calendar is engraved, with the Saint's name for each day. Then a narrow minute ring. Then a silver hour ring of 24

hours. Then a silver band with shutters showing the hours of light and darkness. The centre is occupied by an astrolabe.
A steel hand shows the minutes and gilt hands the hour and age of the moon.
On the back are five small dials, which show the day of the week and of the month and the striking position of the hours and quarters.
The subsidiary clock has a 12-hour dial.
Verge escapement with balance. Spring-driven. Signed 'Johann Schneider Augustae' (Augsburg).
Height of the whole clock 32in. Main clock 8·8in. Subsidiary clock 4in × 3·5in.
See also page 88
See also colour plate V

584c

584a

584b

586 Travelling striking clock movement
Edward East England
Mid 17th century
Gilt dial plate with engraved border and
silver hour ring. Large alarm disc covered
with flowers and foliage. Steel hand not
original.
Verge escapement. Oval pierced cock
covering the balance, screwed to the plate
(original). Fusee and original chain. Silver
count-wheel with blued steel stop-wheels.
Tangent screw set-up. Four-wheel train.
Signed 'Eduardus East Londini'.
Diam 77mm
See also page 88
Presented by Mr Williams, 1825

587 Travelling striking clock
Jacques Duduict France c1640
Gilt case with rounded edge, pierced and
engraved in pattern of flowers and foliage.
Bezel with glass held in by a ring. Clover-
leaf pendant.
Gilt dial with applied silver hour ring.
Engraved scene of Diana and Acteon
inside ring. Engraved pattern of flowers
and foliage outside. Steel hand with long
tail.
Verge escapement. Four-wheel train.
Balance-wheel and spring with index
regulator not original. Ratchet-wheel
replaced. Balance-cock pinned and pegged
to plate. Stopwork for strike missing.
Signed 'Jacques Duduict A Bloys'.
Duduict was married in 1599 and retired
from business in 1645.
Diam 79mm
Presented by C.R. Fletcher Lutwidge,
1874

588 Travelling clock, striking and alarm
Jehan Carquillot France c1660
Silver case. Edge pierced and engraved in
flower pattern. Split bezel. Flat pendant.
White enamel dial. Outer gilt engraved
rim. Gilt alarm disc and hand.
Verge escapement. Three-wheel train.
Stop-work wheels with gilt pierced and
engraved covers. Balance-wheel with
spring, bridge-cock and coqueret
replacements.
Signed 'Jehan Carquillot ABbeuille'.
Diam 98mm

589 Travelling clock, striking and alarm
William Knottesforde England
c1680
Silver case. Back engraved with scene of
the conversion of St Paul. Edge pierced
and engraved in pattern of flowers and
foliage. Round knob pendant.
Dial has an outer ring, gilt and engraved;

then a silver ring for the day of the month
with figures in red; then a gilt turning-ring
with pointer; then a silver alarm disc with
pointer for hour circle. The centre is
engraved with a flower wreath and central
sunflower. Steel hand with long tail.
Verge escapement. Four-wheel train.
Balance spring of $1\frac{1}{4}$ turns with worm-
wheel regulator and silver dial. Cock with
circular table and rimless foot. Silver
count-wheel engraved with sunflower and
filled in with red wax. Steel tracery.
Signed 'William Knottesforde London'.
Knottesforde was a Freeman of the
Clockmakers' Company 1663, Master
1693.
Diam 109mm

590 Celestial globe
Anonymous China c1680–1830
This globe, the maker of which is
unknown, contains clockwork that causes
the globe to rotate in unison with the
heavens. It appears to have been rebuilt at
various dates. The globe is 228mm in
diameter and is brass silver-plated with
engraved lines and stars filled in with
colours. The writing is in Chinese
characters and it was probably made in
China c1680. The movement appears to

have been added in the second half of the
eighteenth century, and is probably
Chinese but is not sufficiently well
designed and constructed to make the
globe a serious astronomical instrument.
The brass stand has four dolphin-shaped
legs and may be of English make as late as
c1830 as the components have Arabic
numeral punchmarks to aid correct
assembly.
Verge escapement, balance and spring.
Fusee.
Nelthropp Collection

591 Table clock, striking and chiming
Johannes Schmidt Germany
Early 18th century
Hexagonal gilt case. Sides with glass in
silvered frames. Silvered caryatid figures
at each angle and silvered lions as feet.
Gilt dial. Silvered hour ring. Two pierced
steel hands. Dial winding.
Verge escapement. Bridge-cock. Engraved
border to top plate and pierced plaque on
it. Engraved hammer heads. Regulator
with SPAD and FRV. Three trains. One bell
with three hammers. Signed 'Johann
Schmidt Baur' (Bamberg).
Diam 150mm Height 95mm
Nelthropp Collection

590

592 Musical table clock
Barraud England c1767
Ebonised case with gilt mounts and arched
top. 10½in high.
Brass engraved back plate with circular
white enamel dial. Gold hands.
Verge escapement with hanging balance-
wheel and cock on back plate. Fusees for
going and musical trains. The clock plays
four tunes on seven bells with nine
hammers (two of the hammers are
duplicated for repeated notes). It also
strikes the hour on a large bell.
Signed 'Barraud London' on back plate
which also has some Chinese characters.
The movement is also stamped 'Thwaites
340' indicating that the movement was
made for Barraud by Thwaites. The
books of Thwaites & Reed show number
340 as having been made in 1767. The
clock is known to have belonged to a
German living in Pekin in 1953.
See C. Jagger, *P.P. Barraud,* pp 106 and
149 and plate XVIII.
Bequeathed to the Company by
Miss E.M. Barraud in 1972.

593 Travelling clock
George Margetts England c1790
Gilt case, the back engine-turned,
covered with translucent blue enamel. An
ivy leaf wreath, a ring of stars and a central
pattern are in gold in the enamel. Edge and
bezel engraved. Oval loop pendant.
White enamel dial signed 'Geo. Margetts
London'. Three subsidiary dials, each
with a domed white enamel centre. Above,
left is the hour dial, I–XII and I–XII and
in the centre 1–24. Right is the minute
circle, with turning minute disc. Below is a
seconds dial with turning seconds disc.
The minutes and seconds discs turn so that
the gold hand on each dial shows mean
time on the fixed and sidereal time on the
turning dial.
Cylinder escapement. Diamond endstone.
Regulator dial on table of solid and
engraved cock. Full plate movement, the
top plate all engraved. Signed 'Geo.
Margetts London 1098'.
Margetts was a Freeman of the
Clockmakers' Company 1779, died 1808.
Diam 96mm
See Rees' *Cyclopaedia* plate XXXIII
which shows a wheel of 487 teeth and
pinion of 80.
See also R.T. Gould, *The Marine
Chronometer,* p 225; *Antiquarian
Horology,* March 1970, for a description of
this and other complicated timekeepers by
Margetts.
Presented by Charles Frodsham & Co,
1875

594 Musical table clock
Anonymous Probably France
Late 18th century
Ebonised rectangular case with ormolu
mounts.
Enamel dial with gilt hands and centre
seconds.
Duplex escapement. A single mainspring
drives the going, striking, quarter chiming
and musical trains. One of four airs is
played after each hour.
10in high and 7in square.
Presented by Miss Troughton in
accordance with the wish of her late
uncle John Grant, 1883

595 Travelling clock, striking, repeating
and alarm
Meuron & Company France
End of 18th century
Silver case. Edge pierced with slight
engraving. Oval loop pendant.
White enamel dial. Steel loop hands. Dial
winding.
Verge escapement. French bridge-cock
with coqueret. Let off repeat by pull-
chain, on bell. Signed 'Meuron & Comp'.
Diam 120mm
Presented by Edward Rogerson, 1892

596 Carriage clock, striking and
repeating
Beguin France c1840
Decorated brass case made in one piece
140mm high. Glass panels. Black leather
travelling case. Circular white enamel
dial signed 'Wertel'. Club-tooth lever
escapement with jewelled pallets.
Helical balance-spring. Strikes hours and
half hours and repeats on a bell.
The back plate is stamped 'J.B. Beguin à
Paris 5'.
See C. Allix, *Carriage Clocks, Their
History and Development,* 1974, p 73
Presented by F. Wilmot, 1957

Marine timekeepers

597 Marine timepiece
Henry Sully France c1724
Burr walnut case like a mantel clock with
carrying handle on top.
Brass dial 127mm diameter with silvered
hour circle and silvered seconds dial.
Engraved 'Henricus Sully Inuenit &
Fecit'. Arrowhead hands. The
escapement is of the frictional rest type
having two semi-circular pallets one above
the other and a single escape-wheel with
teeth not unlike those of a pendulum recoil
escapement. The horizontal balance-staff
is supported on anti-friction wheels.

593

597a

597b

598

Fixed to one end of this staff are cycloid cheeks which thus oscillate to and fro with the balance-wheel. Suspended from these cycloid cheeks is a silk cord, the lower end of which is secured to the middle of a horizontal pendulum pivoted at one end and with a bob at the other. Thus, the oscillation of the balance and its attached cheeks cause the free end of the pendulum to rise and fall. Isochronism was intended to be effected by the contact of the cord on the cycloid cheeks. The clock is spring-driven with a going barrel. Signed on the dial as above. Sully was English, born in 1680, a Freeman of the Clockmakers' Company 1705 and died 1728 having spent nearly all his working life in France. The timepiece, which was predictably

unsuccessful as a marine timekeeper, was sent to George Graham in 1724, with a letter describing it, which is in the Company's library, bound with MS 3981. It is signed 'Sully, Versailles June 29th 1724' and describes the theory of the balance-wheel and horizontal pendulum only. The subsequent history of the clock is not known but it was presented to the Company in 1821 by the clockmaker John Thwaites.

See page 89

See also: Sully's *Description abrégée d'une Horloge d'une nouvelle Invention pour la juste Mesure du Temps sur Mer* (Paris 1726); R.T. Gould, *The Marine Chronometer*, pp 35–9 and plates II and III and fig 9.

598 Marine watch
John Harrison & Son England
1770
Silver pair-case. HM 1768–9. Mahogany carrying case with original cushions which John Harrison preferred to gimbals. White enamel dial with central gold star to turn hands. Centre seconds. Ivory-handled cranked winder. Verge escapement of Harrison's special type having small diamond pallets with the impulse faces set parallel to each other and curved backs on which the escape-wheel teeth also work. Fusee with maintaining power. Remontoire on the fourth wheel wound up every $7\frac{1}{2}$ seconds. Plain steel balance with steel spring and escape-wheel. All wheels from the third onwards are jewelled. Long

bi-metallic strip carried on an adjustable frame. Signed 'John Harrison & Son London 1770 No.2'.
Mechanically, this watch is a near duplicate of John Harrison's prize-winning longitude watch, H.4. It is generally known as 'H.5.' being his fifth marine timekeeper in all. The first four are all at the National Maritime Museum, Greenwich. This watch was in the Shandon Collection before being purchased by the Company.
See page 89
For illustrations and technical and historical descriptions, see: *Horological Journal* December 1955, p 804; *Pioneers of Precision Timekeeping*, Antiquarian Horological Society (1964), pp 7–8 and 19–29. R.T. Gould, *The Marine Chronometer*, pp 65–6 and plates XIII and XIV; H. Quill, *John Harrison, the Man who found Longitude.*
See also colour plate V

599 Marine chronometer
John Arnold   England
Probably 1771 and later
Octagonal box without gimbals.
Silvered dial with subsidiary seconds dial.
Spring detent escapement. Two-arm compensation balance. Fusee and chain.
Sun and planet maintaining power.
One-day going. Signed 'Iohn Arnold London No 1'.
See also page 90
This problematical timekeeper, like many others by John Arnold, was subsequently brought up to date by him, possibly on more than one occasion. For a full discussion of its date and history see V. Mercer, *John Arnold & Son*, pp 35–9 and plates 42–5.

600 Marine chronometer
John Arnold   England   c1775 and later
White enamel dial. Subsidiary seconds dial. Octagonal box without gimbals.
Spring detent escapement. z balance. Fusee.
Signed 'John Arnold London Invt. et Fect. No. 14'.
See also page 90
Like No 1, above, this is a very early Arnold which would have started life with a pivoted detent and was subsequently rebuilt by Arnold, probably c1790.
Presented by Charles Frodsham & Co, 1875

601 Marine chronometer
Brockbanks   England   c1785
Box with gimbals.
Enamel dial.

Peto cross-detent escapement. Three-arm compensation balance. Fusee.
Signed 'Brockbanks London' (no number).
See also page 90
Presented by Samuel E. Atkins, 1875

602 Marine chronometer
Josiah Emery   England   1792
Brass case somewhat like a small bracket clock, engraved on the base 'No. 1', with wood, baize-lined travelling case.
Vertical white enamel dial with three subsidiary dials and gold hands for hours, minutes and seconds.
Constant-force escapement. Unlocking is

performed by a lever. The escape-wheel tensions two helical springs attached to two arbors with impulse pallets, and these give impulse to the balance. The balance has four bi-metallic arms and runs in friction rollers with diamond endstones. Fusee. Signed 'Josiah Emery Charing Cross London No.1'.
This is the surviving one of four similar machines made by Emery and submitted for trial at Greenwich in 1792.
See also page 90
For illustrations and a description of its many unusual features see *Antiquarian Horology*, June 1961, pp 206–7.
Presented by Percy Webster, 1923

602a

603 Marine chronometer
John Arnold & Son England c1795
Octagonal kingwood case without gimbals.
Silvered dial. Subsidiary seconds dial.
Spring detent escapement. 8-day
movement. Going barrel. z balance.
Helical steel spring with end-curves. The
balance spring is underneath the balance
and in tension so as to relieve friction on
the lower pivot. Signed 'John Arnold &
Son London No $\frac{78}{168}$ Invt. et Fect'.
Nelthropp Collection

604 Marine chronometer
John Arnold England c1795
Octagonal case without gimbals.
Silvered 4in dial with subsidiary seconds
dial.
Spring detent. Helical spring with
terminal curves. oz balance.
Signed 'John Arnold & Son London
No.92 Invt et Fect'.
Presented by A.E. Rutherford 1909

605 Marine chronometer
John Arnold & Son England c1795
Octagonal wood case with glass at bottom
and sides without gimbals.
White enamel dial. Subsidiary seconds
dial. Signed 'John Arnold & Son London
No.101'.
Spring detent escapement. z balance.
Gold balance spring. Fusee.
2-day movement. Signed 'John Arnold &
Son London No.101/191'.
Presented by Charles Frodsham & Co,
1875

606 Marine chronometer
Howells & Pennington England
c1795
Octagonal brass case with glass sides and
bottom. Gilt dial plate with two subsidiary
enamel dials, one for hours and minutes
and the other for seconds. The dials are
surrounded with pierced and carved silver
filigree decoration. 36-hour movement.
Mudge's constant-force escapement. The
balance pivots run between anti-friction
wheels. Plain balance and compensation
curb. The mainspring barrel is of the
standing type, the fusee chain being
hooked to an outer dummy barrel fixed to
the rotating mainspring arbor.
Signed 'Howells & Pennington for Thos.
Mudge 1795 No 7'.
This is one of the timekeepers made in a
workshop set up by Thomas Mudge
Junior to make them on his father's plan.
About fifteen seem to have been made but
they did not perform as well as the marine
timekeepers made by Mudge Senior, and

602b

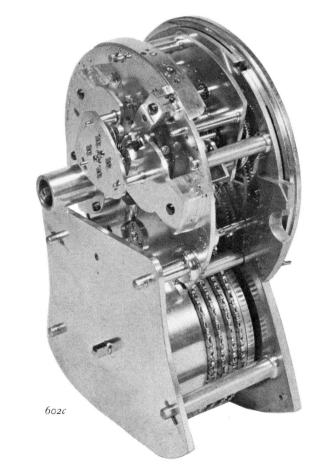

602c

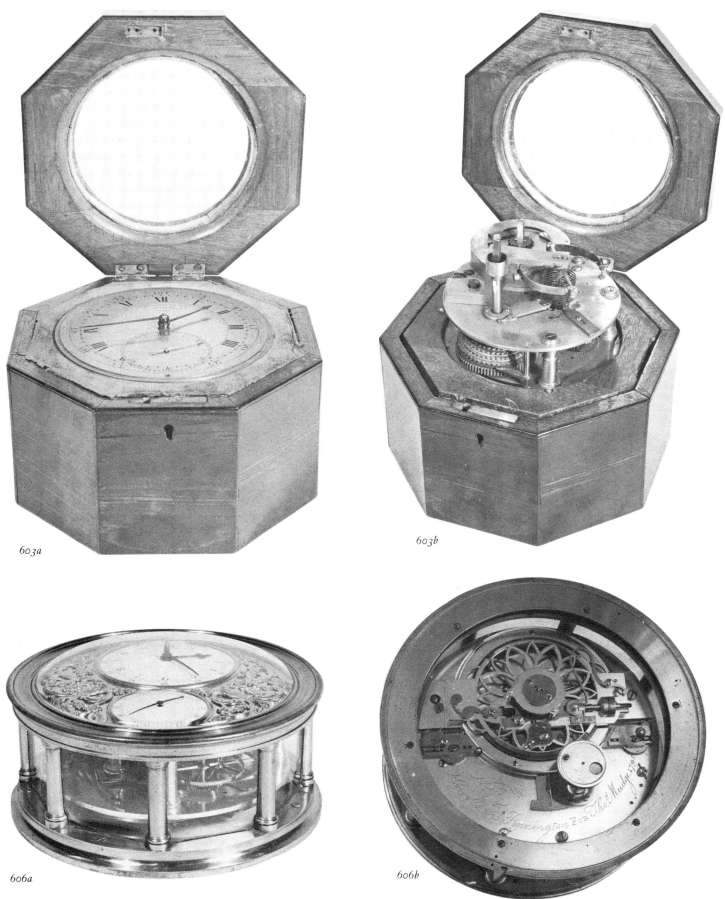

603a

603b

606a

606b

they were unsuccessful mainly due to the cost of manufacture (£157), this figure being undercut by Arnold & Earnshaw (£65).
See also numbers 630, 631, and page
See R.T. Gould, *The Marine Chronometer*, pp 81–2.

607 Marine chronometer
George Margetts England
End of 18th century
Brass case.
White enamel dial, apparently unsigned, but in a strong light the ghost of the signature 'Margetts' is visible, having evidently been stoned off for some unknown reason.
Spring detent escapement. Compensation balance. As an endstone for the balance-staff there is an agate disc, turned once in five hours by the great wheel, to distribute the wear of the pivots. 8-day movement. No signature on the movement, but the number 102.
See page 90
See *Antiquarian Horology*, March 1970, pp 355–6

608 Marine chronometer
Vissière France End of 18th century
Box with gimbals. Bottom of brass case weighted.
Enamel dial diameter 78mm. Centre seconds with hour and minute rings and up-and-down indicator.
Spring detent escapement. Two-arm compensation balance. Helical balance-spring without terminal curves.
Signed 'Vissière Argenteuil (Seine et Oise) No.121'.
Nelthropp Collection

609 Marine chronometer
Robert Molyneux England
Early 19th century
Box with gimbals.
One-day movement. Spring detent escapement. Two-arm compensation balance. Helical balance-spring with terminal curves. Signed 'Robt. Molyneux London No 526'.
For particulars of Molyneux's work see *Antiquarian Horology*, June 1972, pp 607–12.
Bequeathed by S.E. Atkins, 1898

610 Marine chronometer
William Hardy England
Early 19th century
Box with gimbals.
Possibly an experimental piece. Pivoted detent escapement. Hardy's type of balance, consisting of a bi-metallic bar with uprights supporting weights at each end. Helical balance-spring. Going barrel. Signed 'Wm. Hardy Invt. et Fect. London No.2'.
On loan from the Corporation of the City of London

611 Marine chronometer
Anonymous England
Early 19th century
Circular brass case.
Enamel dial with hour circle above and seconds dial below.
Arnold-type spring detent escapement. Plain two-arm balance with compensation by bi-metallic strips which vary the gap between the curb-pins. Helical balance spring without end-curves. Resting barrel.
Nelthropp Collection

612 Marine chronometer
John Roger Arnold England c1802
Gimballed in box with slide shutter and rating certificate.
Silvered 75mm dial with central minute hand and subsidiary dials for hours and seconds.
Arnold's spring detent escapement. z balance. One-day movement.
Signed 'John R. Arnold London Invt. et Fecit No.297'.
John Roger Arnold, son of John, was a Freeman of the Clockmakers' Company 1796, Master 1817, died 1843.
See V. Mercer, *John Arnold & Son*, p 219

613 Marine chronometer
John Roger Arnold England c1805
Gimballed mahogany box with ivory-mounted key.
Silvered dial. Subsidiary dial for seconds and up-and-down indicator. Arnold's spring detent escapement. Later balance and spring. 8-day movement.
Signed 'John R. Arnold. London. Invt. et Fecit. No 312'.
See V. Mercer, *John Arnold & Son*, p 219

614 Marine chronometer
John Roger Arnold England c1809
Gimballed box.
Silvered 80mm dial with central seconds hand and subsidiary dials for hours and minutes.
Arnold's spring detent escapement. Later two-arm compensation balance. Helical balance-spring with adjustable stud. Going barrel. One-day movement.
Signed 'John R. Arnold London Invt. et Fecit No 344'.
See V. Mercer, *John Arnold & Son*, p 219
Presented by S.E. Atkins, 1891

615 Marine chronometer
Brockbanks England c1810
Gimballed mahogany box.
White enamel dial.
Spring detent escapement. The passing-spring is planted separately from the detent yet it is not a Peto cross-detent of the type generally favoured by Brockbanks. It has a special over-banking arrangement. Three-arm compensation balance, with stops limiting the movement of the arms.
Signed 'Brockbanks London No.568'.
Presented by S.E. Atkins, 1896

616 Marine chronometer
Brockbanks & Atkins England
After 1815
Gimballed box
Enamel 90mm dial. Gold hands. One-day movement.
Spring detent escapement. Three-arm compensation balance with movement of the arms limited by stop. Helical balance-spring. Signed 'Brockbanks & Atkins London No.872'.
Myles Brockbank was a Freeman of the Clockmakers' Company 1776. George Atkins was admitted 1788, Master 1845, died 1855.
Nelthropp Collection

617 Marine chronometer
Barrauds England c1822
Mahogany box with gimbals.
Engraved silver dial. Subsidiary dials for seconds and up-and-down dial, diameter 88mm. Eight-day movement.
Spring detent. Two-arm balance with stops limiting movement. Barrel raised above top plate by a cock. Fixed winding key. Signed 'Barrauds Cornhill London 997'.
See C. Jagger, *P.P. Barraud*, p 134.
Bequeathed by S.E. Atkins, 1898

618 Marine chronometer
Clement Harris England c1825
Box with sprung gimbals.
Silvered dial. Subsidiary dials for seconds and up-and-down.
Spring detent escapement. Two-arm compensation balance. Helical balance-spring. 8-day movement. Signed 'Harris late Hatton & Harris London 660'.
Harris was a Freeman of the Clockmakers' Company 1816.
Presented by S.E. Atkins, 1894

619a

619 Marine chronometer
Joseph Croucher England c1830
Gimballed box 13¾in square.
Brass 6½in dial with hour and minute
circle above and seconds dial below.
Up-and-down indicator. 30-hour
movement.
Ulrich's special constant-force escapement
of extreme complication with 7 spring
detents as described in his patent
specification 5639 of 19th April 1828.
Complicated compensation balance of
brass and platinum.
Croucher was a Freeman of the
Clockmakers' Company in 1827.
See also page 90
See R.T. Gould, *The Marine Chronometer*,
p 142.
See *Analytical hints on the patent marine
timekeeper made by Joseph Croucher*
(Copy in Clockmakers' Company
Library)

619b

620 Marine chronometer
E. Barthet France c1840
Gimballed box.
Silvered 80mm dial with central minute
hand and subsidiary dials for hours and
seconds; also a thermometer.
Spring detent escapement with endwise
adjustment. Two-arm compensation
balance. Barrel-shaped balance-spring.
Fusee chain with double links. 30-hour
movement. Signed 'E. Barthet
A Marseille No.10'.
This chronometer, of exceptionally high
quality, was picked up at sea from an
abandoned ship by Sir William Walker in
1846, when in command of the *Monarch*.
It was purchased from him by Messrs
Brockbanks & Atkins for £15 and
presented by Samuel E. Atkins in 1875.

621 Marine chronometer
James Ferguson Cole England 1840
Gimballed box.   80mm dial.
Cole's double rotary spring detent
escapement. Flat spiral spring with
overcoil of four turns. Going barrel.
Goes 3 days. Male winding key.
Signed 'James F. Cole Invt. London
AD 1840 Double Rotary Detached
Escapement'.
See R.T. Gould, *The Marine
Chronometer*, p 139
Nelthropp Collection

622 Marine chronometer
John Poole England
Mid 19th century
Gimballed box.
Silvered 100mm dial. Up-and-down
indicator.
Spring detent escapement. Balance with
Poole's auxiliary compensation, being the
first auxiliary applied to chronometer
balances. Signed 'John Poole Maker to the
Admiralty 57 Fenchurch Street London
3274'.
Nelthropp Collection

623 Marine chronometer
E.J. Dent England Mid 19th century
Gimballed box. Two-day movement.
Silvered 96mm dial with subsidiary
seconds dial and up-and-down indicator.
Spring detent escapement. Dent's
balance, consisting of a bi-metallic bar
with a U-shaped bi-metallic strip at each
end. The U is horizontal, one leg being
attached to the bar while the other
carries a weight, designed to provide
auxiliary compensation. Helical balance-
spring with end curves. Signed 'Dent
London Chronometer Maker to the
Queen No 1815'.
Nelthropp Collection

624 Marine chronometer
Fletcher England c1860
This eight-day chronometer lacks gimbals
and its box.
The dial which has a sloped bezel is signed
'Fletcher. 48 Lombard Street No.200' but
the movement is signed 'Fletcher
27 Davies St. London'. It was probably
made by John Fletcher who supplied the
trade and who took over from J.S. Eiffe
when the latter retired while working at
48 Lombard Street.
See *Britten's Old Clocks & Watches &
their Makers*, (6th edition), p 747
Bequeathed by T. Vickery, 1946

625 Marine chronometer
George Blackie England After 1862
Rosewood box.
Spring detent escapement. Two-arm
compensation balance with short upright
bi-metallic strips carrying vertical weights
at the ends of the arms. The balance is
mounted on a separate plate below the top
plate. Eight-day movement. Signed
'George Blackie 24 Amwell Street London
Prize Medal 1862 No 822'. The prize was
awarded for the auxiliary compensation
balance as described above.
Nelthropp Collection

Miscellaneous clocks, sundials and other items

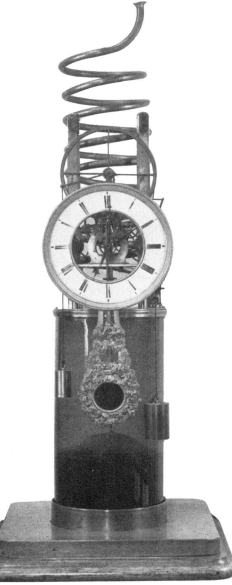

626

This category of the Company's Collection embraces many interesting and diversified items that are supplementary to the clocks and watches already described, and it includes three clocks that cannot be properly placed in any of the clock sections. For instance, there is number 626, a pin-pallet spring driven pendulum table clock by P. Andervalt of Trieste that is re-wound automatically by the pressure of hydrogen gas. Its appearance is quite unlike that of any other clock, mainly because of the coiled brass tube surmounting the mechanism, as can be seen in the illustration.

Another singular clock is number 627 one of the earliest examples of an electric clock and is signed and numbered by its Scottish inventor, Alexander Bain. He designed and built the original of these clocks in 1846 when electrical knowledge was so much in its infancy that Bain himself referred to the 'electric fluid' and the terms 'in series' and 'in parallel' had not yet come into general use. Although Bain was the first to apply electricity to drive a pendulum, Steinheil in Germany anticipated him in the transmission of time signals to secondary clocks by his Bavarian patent dated October 2nd 1839.

The Collection contains seven working models of clock and watch escapements, including examples of Mudge's elaborate constant-force device. These escapement models are particularly helpful to students as in each example the principles of how the mechanism operates are far easier to follow than is possible from looking at a completed timekeeper.

Clock- and watch-making tools are one of the weakest sections of the Collection, but this is to some extent offset by the fine variety of exhibits of chronometer balances as well as watch and chronometer balance-springs of the eighteenth, nineteenth and twentieth centuries, including one of the rare spherical chronometer balance springs constructed by the hand of E. Dent, catalogue number 639.

The sundial was the earliest form of timekeeper, and even up to the end of the eighteenth century pocket sundials were far more common as time-tellers than watches, which in those days were not any more accurate and yet cost a great deal more money. Sundials of very great variety have been produced, but the Company's small collection of seventeen examples is confined to four main types: tablet, diptych or folding dials, universal equatorial dials, ring dials, horizontal dials. Included in the last group are the decorative silver pocket types known as 'Butterfield dials', so named after an Englishman who worked in France and Paris from 1677 to his death in 1724, see catalogue numbers 658–61. Because of the ununiform path followed by the earth in its journey around the sun, a sundial can only provide an approximate estimation of mean time and if greater accuracy should be required recourse has to be made to tables of the equation of time, examples of which can be seen in an earlier part of the catalogue (numbers 649, 102 and 553).

Although the Barton button described in number 674 has no connection with clocks and watches, nevertheless the maker, Sir John Barton of the Royal Mint, was an important figure as he married the only daughter of John Harrison (1693–1776) and after her death nearly all the Harrison relics now owned by the Company passed into his custody.

The Company's large collection of watch keys is a most important one containing examples that cover three centuries and including English and continental keys

Watch key, detail from illustration *681d*

many of which are highly decorative. To date a watch key with any accuracy is difficult, as none has any indication of the year, such as a hallmark stamped on them, and not even the shape of the earliest keys is known with any certainty. The earliest illustration of a simple cranked key appears in the picture painted c1605 by an unknown artist of the 'Tasburgh Group' which was on view to the public at the *Elizabethan Image* exhibition at the Tate Gallery, 1969–70. Whether or not a specific key is original to its watch is very difficult to determine unless the key displays piercing or some other form of decoration which clearly matches up with a similar design applied to the watch itself.

The wristwatch, which has now almost completely replaced the pocket watch, had crude beginnings. Initially, at a date around 1908, small pocket or ladies' watches were adapted to be worn on the wrist by being placed in a small round leather container integral with the wrist strap, see catalogue number 684. The 1914 war produced another clumsy but extremely useful device for the wristwatch wearer and was designed to protect the fragile watch glass of that period from breakage which occurred all too frequently in the trenches. It consisted of a metal grill to cover the face of the watch and was kept in position by lugs through which the wristwatch strap was threaded (see catalogue number 685). It is interesting to note that this device was to all intents and purposes very similar to that employed in the earliest watches made around 1580–1610 which, of course, had no glass, the figures on the dial being observed through the openwork piercing of the hinged front cover of the watch (see catalogue numbers 1 to 4).

Miscellaneous clocks, sundials and other items

626 Gas-operated clock
Pasquale Andervalt Italy c1835
Skeleton frame. Enamel dial with open centre to expose the mechanism. Steel hands. Pin-pallet escapement and decorative gilt pendulum. The motive power is a small brass weight which, when nearly run down, is wound up by the pressure of hydrogen gas created by a ball of zinc being automatically released from the coiled brass tubular magazine. The zinc ball falls into the red glass jar which contains dilute sulphuric acid, and the gas thus formed lifts a piston which raises all the visible mechanism behind the dial and the going weight is thereby wound. This winding process is slow, and while it is taking place the smaller brass weight acts as a maintaining power and keeps the clock going. Clock and jar 36in high. Signed 'Pasquale Andervalt'.
Presented by William Wing, 1874
Illustrated on page 105

627 Electrically-driven clock
Alexander Bain British c1846–50
The seconds pendulum carries a coil in the large heavy cylindrical bob which is energised every alternate swing by means of sliding bar contacts and this makes it interact with two bar magnets to maintain the motion. A crutch driven by the pendulum advances a ratchet-wheel, thus driving the hands through a reduction train. Originally, Bain made use of an earth battery formed by a zinc plate and a copper plate buried in moist earth to supply the working current. Later on this was usually replaced by a wet Leclanché cell.
Oak case designed for wall mounting, 70in high. Silvered dial 11in in diameter. Signed 'Alexander Bain Patentee No. 235'.
Alexander Bain (1810–77) was a Scotsman who came to London in 1837 as a journeyman clockmaker after spending some years in Edinburgh. His English patent, applied for on October 10th 1840, was the first to apply electricity for driving a pendulum.
Bequeathed by A.W. Marshall, 1973
See Alexander Bain, *A short history of the electric clocks with explanations of their principles*, (1852, reprinted 1973); F. Hope-Jones, *Electrical Timekeeping*, (1949). *Antiquarian Horology*, December 1974, pp 51–63.
Bequeathed by A.W. Marshall, 1973

628 Conical pendulum clock
Anonymous [France] c1835
The movement is on a wooden stand covered by a glass dome. A clock with a conical or rotating pendulum requires no escapement and is self-starting. The train of wheels ends in a horizontal finger which touches an extension on the bottom of the pendulum weight which is suspended by a thread and gives it a continuous circular motion. This 30-hour clock lacks the refinements necessary for accuracy. As early as 1660 Christiaan Huygens experimented with a clock having a conical pendulum.
Presented by G.S. Sanders, 1971

629 Galileo's pendulum escapement
This model represents the mechanism devised by Galileo about 1641. The ingenious escapement can be seen clearly. The model is spring-driven although Galileo's design was weight driven.
Made and presented by **Inkerman Rogers**

630 Constant-force escapement
[**Thomas Mudge**] England c1785
Parts of a constant-force escapement taken from one of Mudge's early marine chronometers or possibly a clock. The balance is very large, 56mm diameter, and is complete with its cranked balance-staff and a gold helical balance-spring. There is also the constant-force escape-wheel with double spiral springs and cocks.

631 Constant-force escapement
[**Howells & Pennington**] England c1795
Plain brass plate 110mm diameter mounted with a complete balance, cock and constant-force escapement identical with that in the Howells & Pennington marine timekeeper, catalogue number 606. It must originally have formed part of a chronometer and although not signed was almost certainly made by Howells & Pennington. The escapement is now mounted on a brass stand with three legs.
Presented by Charles Frodsham & Co, 1873

632 Duplex escapement
Anonymous England c1795
It has double escape-wheels and the whole escapement is fitted to the top plate of a watch.

633 Duplex escapement
Anonymous England c1850
A platform escapement fitted with a 'Chinese' double resting tooth type of duplex.
Presented by E.J. Thompson, 1895

634 Chronometer escapement
W.T. Heyes England 1903
A normal-sized marine chronometer escapement mounted as an exhibition model. It won the first prize offered by the Clockmakers' Company in 1903 for excellence of workmanship.
See *Horological Journal*, February 1903, p 75

635 Lever escapement
A.J. Barnsdale England c1910
A large demonstration model.
Presented by W. Barnsdale, 1913

636 Balances 19th and 20th centuries
Various types taken from marine chronometers including examples by Arnold, Airy, Berthoud, Dent, Ditisheim, Hartnup, Kulberg, Le Roy, Mercer, Molyneux and others not identified.

637 Balance and spring
T. Earnshaw England c1810
Taken from an early Earnshaw marine chronometer.
Presented by W.B. Crisp, 1887

638 Balance-spring
John Hammersley England c1875
'Trio in Uno' type.
Presented by Thomas Hewett, 1905

639 Balance-springs
19th and 20th centuries
a) Flat, helical and spherical balance-springs suitable for marine chronometers, mounted on an exhibition stand. Made c1840 by **E.J. Dent** (1790–1853), Royal Exchange, London.
b) Flat, overcoil and helical balance-springs for watches, mounted on an exhibition stand. Made c1890 by Daniel Buckney (1845–1927), Kings Square, London.
Presented by E. Dent & Company, 1973

640 Sector England c1780
A proportional gauge for finding out the correct proportions between the diameter of a wheel and that of the correct pinion to gear with it. Made by **R. Pennington**.
Presented by George Blackie, 1884

641 Gauge for pivoting arbors
18th century
One end was set to the height between the plates and the other end gave the length for pivoting.
Presented by W. Barnsdale, 1915

642 Micrometer gauge 19th century
For inside and outside measurements.
Presented by George Blackie, 1884

643 Maintaining-power bolt England
18th century
The bolt of a maintaining-power device for a clock. A string was pulled before winding thereby causing the bolt or detent arm to engage with a tooth of a wheel and exert spring pressure which kept the clock going during winding.
Presented by W. Barnsdale 1915

644 Fusee chains
Thomas Mercer Ltd England
20th century
Ten examples of watch and clock fusee chains.
Presented by Thomas Mercer Ltd

645 Alarm attachment
Isaac Court England c1800
The spring-driven alarm mechanism is contained in a black tin box and includes a clip to hold a key-wound watch. The winding square of the watch fits a key which forms part of the alarm mechanism, and it is the turning of the fusee while unwinding that trips the alarm at a pre-determined time.
Presented by S.E. Atkins, 1875

646 Water clock
Anonymous Ceylon Unknown
A copper bowl, 120mm diameter, which has a hole bushed with gold in the bottom. In use it was floated on water and when it sank a period of about 25 minutes had elapsed. No time scale is engraved.

647 Hour glasses
Anonymous [France]
Late 18th century
a) 4-hour glass, 330mm high, and is probably pre-1750.
b) 2-hour glass, 215mm high, and is probably 1750–80. Both glasses are in oak frames with turned pillars, and are likely to be of French make for use at sea.
Nelthropp Collection

648 Astrolabe
Hamid Indo-Persian 1688
The astrolabe was used for astronomical observations, time-telling and surveying, and is an instrument of great antiquity. This particular astrolabe is brass, 85mm diameter, and was made in Lahore, India (latitude 31° 40′N) although the engraving is in Persian characters. There are two plates engraved with projections of the celestial sphere each for a different latitude, and these are covered by a

cut-away plate, the *rete*, which indicates the position of the brightest stars. The rule or movable sighting arm, the central pivot and its wedge are all missing. This astrolabe is signed and dated on the back just below the ring by which it can be suspended.
Nelthropp Collection

649 Table of Equation of Time 1717
Signed by John Harrison (1693–1776) and mounted on the inside of part of a soft-wood clock door. This door almost certainly formed part of the original case (now lost) of the clock dated 1717 and made by John Harrison which is now at Nostell Priory, Yorkshire. It is of almost identical construction to number 551. Presented by the Royal Greenwich Observatory, Hurstmonceux.
See T. North, *The Church Bells of the City and County of Lincoln*, p 61. Also, H. Quill, *John Harrison, The Man who found Longitude*, fig 6.

650 Sundial
J3K [Jacob Karner, Nürnberg]
Germany c1630
Tablet, folding or diptych dial. Ivory 91 × 63mm. Outside of the lid is engraved with the cardinal points surrounded by a 1–32 scale and pointer, also a hole for viewing the compass when taking bearings. Inner surface of lid engraved in red and black with 24 names of towns and latitudes, also a declination dial marked with the length of day and appropriate sign of the Zodiac. Thread gnomon. Inside of lower leaf has a compass (missing) surrounded by a horizontal dial marked for four latitudes, and below it are two scales for unequal hours. On the bottom surface are circular tables for Julian and Gregorian epacts. In the centre there was probably a rotating dial, possibly lunar, which is now missing. There is a recess in the side of the base which may have been used to store style pins or even a wind vane.
Nelthropp Collection

651 Sundial
Anonymous [France (Dieppe)]
Late 17th century
Tablet, folding or diptych dial. Ivory 80 × 65mm. Outside of lid is engraved with polar and equatorial dials; used in conjunction is a scale of latitudes engraved on the right edge of the inside of the lid and a folding metal strut. Also on the inside of the lid is a pewter lunar volvelle. Thread gnomon. The compass rose which is recessed on the inside of the bottom is marked with the latitudes and names of towns, and is surmounted by a silvered elliptical azimuth hour scale, the latter being set by moving a pewter perpetual calendar on the outside of the base. Surrounding the compass (glass and needle missing) is a horizontal dial.
Nelthropp Collection

652 Sundial
T.W. 1600
Universal equatorial pocket dial. Oval watch-shaped of gilt metal 54 × 45mm with hinged hour ring. Compass (later) and plumb line. Engraved list of latitudes which includes Gibraltar which is very unusual for the date 1600. Signed 'T.W. Fecit 1600'.
Nelthropp Collection

653 Sundial
J. Schretteger German c1700
Universal equatorial pocket dial. Octagonal brass 56mm overall with hinged hour ring and hinged gnomon. Compass dial is a replacement. Signed 'Johan Schretteger in Augsberg'.
Nelthropp Collection

654 Sundial
Lorenz Grassl German c1700
Universal equatorial pocket dial. Octagonal brass 50mm overall with hour circle hinged to move against a sector engraved with a scale of latitudes. The latitudes of Leipzig, Cologne, Strasbourg and Pisa engraved on the back. Signed 'L. Grassl'.
Nelthropp Collection

655 Sundial
Lorenz Grassl German c1700
Universal equatorial pocket dial. Octagonal brass 80mm overall. Hour circle hinged to move against a sector of latitudes. Many latitudes engraved on the back. Wind vane. Signed 'Lorenz Grassl in Augsberg'.
Nelthropp Collection

656 Sundial
A. Chevallier France c1840
Universal equatorial pocket dial. Octagonal brass 70mm overall, with hinged silvered hour ring. Signed 'A. Chevallier Opticien Rue de la Bourse No. 1 à Paris'.
Nelthropp Collection

657 Sundial
Anonymous England c1800
Universal equatorial portable dial. Circular brass 116mm diam with hinged silvered hour circle and gnomon. Compass. Two sets of figures are engraved, one for southern latitudes.
Nelthropp Collection

658 Sundial
Butterfield France
Early 18th century
Horizontal pocket dial. Silver octagonal 78 × 66mm. Compass and four horizontal hour scales for different northern latitudes. The folding style which is shaped like a bird is adjustable to various latitudes from 40° to 60°N. The user adjusts the style to the correct latitude and then aligns it to the celestial pole by means of the compass and the time can then be read on the appropriate hour scale.
Presented by Mr Batt, 1876

659 Sundial
Butterfield France
Early 18th century
Horizontal pocket dial. Silver octagonal 66 × 56mm. It is similar to catalogue number 658.
Nelthropp Collection

660 Sundial
P. Seuin France Early 18th century
Horizontal pocket dial of the Butterfield type. Octagonal silver 53 × 40mm with compass and hinged adjustable gnomon. The latitudes of 24 places are engraved on the back. Signed 'P. Seuin A Paris'.
Presented by John Grant, 1852

661 Sundial
Nicholas Bion France
Early 18th century
Horizontal pocket dial of the Butterfield type. Octagonal silver with compass and adjustable hinged gnomon graduated for latitudes 40° to 60°N. The back is engraved with the latitudes of 23 places in Europe.
Length 70mm
Presented by A.W. Marshall, 1970

662 Sundial
T. Menant France 1743
Horizontal dial of fixed type made for the latitude of 45°N. Brass, 175mm square. Originally a compass was fitted but card and needle now missing.
Signed 'Menant Paris 1743'.
Nelthropp Collection

663 Sundial
Anonymous c1800
Horizontal dial of the portable type.
Circular brass 100mm diam with hinged
gnomon. No adjustment for latitude but
was designed for use in about latitude
52°s.

664 Sundial
Anonymous Late 17th century
Single ring pocket altitude dial. Brass
38mm diam. The time is shown on the
inside of the ring by the sun's ray passing
through a hole in a slide which is adjusted
to the day of the month engraved on a
scale on the outside of the ring.

665 Sundial
E. Nairne England c1760
Universal ring dial. Brass, 155mm diam.
The meridian ring is engraved for
northern and southern latitudes while the
central bridge has a date scale on one side
and a scale of the sun's declination on the
other. In addition to finding solar time the
dial has a subsidiary use of obtaining the
altitude of the sun. To do this the altitude
scale is set to 0° and, then, if a wire is put
in a hole at 45°s on the meridan ring and
the dial turned on edge the shadow of the
wire falls on an altitude scale engraved on
the back of the meridian ring.
Signed 'E. Nairne London'.
Bequeathed by T. Vickery, 1946

666 Compass
R.B. Bate England c1800
Contained in an oval watch-shaped gilt
case with pendant approximately 50mm
diam. The compass dial is enamel.
Signed 'Bate London'.
Nelthropp Collection

667 Pedometer
Benjamin Gray England c1755
Silver case and dial 45mm diam. The
central hand indicates up to 100 steps
($\frac{1}{10}$th mile) and the three small dials
recording up to 1 mile, 10 miles and 100
miles respectively. Inscribed 'Made by
B. Gray clockmaker to George 2nd. Given
to the Company of Clockmakers by his
great-grandson B.L. Vulliamy 1849'.

668 Pedometer
Benjamin Gray England
HM 1754–5
Silver case, 56mm diam. Central hand and
three smaller hands, similar to catalogue
number 667 but lacking dial and

operating push piece. Inscribed 'Made by
B. Gray clockmaker to George 2nd. Given
to Charles Frodsham by his great-
grandson B.L. Vulliamy 1849'.
Presented by Charles Frodsham & Co,
1875.

669 Pedometer
Fraser England HM 1788–9
Silver-gilt case, diam 56mm. Engraved
on the back with a ducal coronet and the
letter s. A long hand on the dial indicates
up to 100 steps and a smaller dial records
miles.
Signed 'Fraser Bond Street London'.
Nelthropp Collection

670 Pedometer
Spencer & Perkins England
Late 18th century
Worn at the waistband and operated by
the forward movement of the thigh. The
white enamel dial has a large central hand
which indicates up to 100 steps ($\frac{1}{10}$th mile).
The small left-hand dial records up to
1,000 steps and the right-hand dial up to
12 miles. The instrument is complete
with its box, wash-leather pouch and
printed instructions. Signed 'Spencer &
Perkins London' (on dial), and 1291 is
stamped on the actuating lever.

671 Pedometer
Spencer & Perkins England
Late 18th century
Gilt case with enamel dial. Diam 56mm. It
is very similar to catalogue number 670,
and is reputed to have been formerly the
property of Queen Charlotte.
Signed 'Spencer & Perkins London'.
Presented by B.L. Vulliamy, 1849

672 Cyclometer
Thomas Eayre England
Mid 18th century
An instrument for measuring the distance
run by a carriage. Gilt dial 140mm square
with silvered mile circle. Two steel hands
one for furlongs and the other for miles,
also a bell for indicating miles. Operated
by a shaft at the top.
Signed 'Tho. Eayre Kett' (Kettering).
Nelthropp Collection

673 Cyclometer
John Brockbank England
Late 18th century
Brass dial, diam 104mm with two hands to
show up to 100 and 10,000 yards and a

small dial to show up to 30,000 yards.
There is a shaft with a star wheel operated
by a wheel of the carriage. It was made by
Brockbank for his own use and attached to
his gig.
Presented by Samuel E. Atkins, 1875

674 Barton button
Sir John Barton England c1822
In 1822, Sir John Barton was granted a
patent for his method of engraving steel
buttons with 2,000 lines to the inch. The
extreme closeness of these lines broke up
the reflected light so as to produce a
rainbow effect. This invention was the
forerunner of the diffraction grating (see
number 675) which in conjunction with
the spectrograph is used for the
investigation and identification of matter.
Sir John Barton (1771–1834) was Deputy
Controller of the Royal Mint, Treasurer to
Queen Adelaide and married Ann the
daughter of John Harrison of longitude
fame. Barton was a friend of Maudslay
who probably made for him his straight-
line ruling engine (now in the Science
Museum, South Kensington, London)
with which Barton made his iridescent
buttons.
See *A Ruling Engine used by Sir John
Barton*, a paper read by P. Grodzinski
before the Newcomen Society,
January 14th 1948.

675 Diffraction grating
Anonymous Australia 1963
A steel plate engraved with parallel lines at
equal intervals at 1,008 lines to the inch.
A beam of light falling on such a grating is
resolved into a spectrum. It enables two
wavelengths very close together to be
separated. See also catalogue number 674.
Presented by Z.A.M. Merfield,
Aeronautical Research Laboratory,
Melbourne, Australia, 1963

676 Money-box
Cylindrical iron money-box formerly used
by the Company

677 Watch-hooks England 1825–40
Ladies wore their watches suspended from
the waist on watch hooks of this type.
These hooks were superseded in fashion by
watch brooches.
Nelthropp Collection

678 Steel seal England 18th century
Engraved with a clock dial, the hands
showing 3 o'clock. 35mm diameter.
Nelthropp Collection

679 Silver seal England c1840
Fine silver seal engraved with the armorial
bearings of the Worshipful Company of
Clockmakers. Oval 48 × 42mm.

680 **Quare** signet ring England c1850
Gold signet ring set with a bloodstone
engraved with crest and motto 'Facta
non verba'.
Presented by the executor of L.B. Quare
who had it from Horace Quare, his uncle,
who was the last direct descendant of
Daniel Quare.

681 Watch keys, seals and fobs
17th, 18th and 19th centuries
A collection of twenty tortoiseshell
frames containing watch keys (15 frames),
seals (2 frames), fobs and chatelaines
(3 frames).
Bequeathed by the widow of Philip Hill
and a further collection presented by
Sidney Sanders.

682 Presentation key England 1893
Gold key modelled to represent the arms
of the Clockmakers' Company with
enamelled shield. In a case fitted with a
silver plate inscribed 'Presented to the
Rev. H.L. Nelthropp M.A., F.S.A.,
Master of the Company of Clockmakers
by the Committee of the Clock &
Watchmakers Asylum, on the occasion of
the opening of a widow's House at New
Southgate which had been endowed by
the Company of Clockmakers . . . 1893'.

683 Watch hands
James Haswell England c1900
A frame, 900 × 250mm, containing two
panels on which are mounted a display of
watch hands made by James Haswell,
49 Spencer Street, London.
Presented by J. Eric Haswell, his son

684 Wristwatch strap England c1908
Early leather wrist strap designed to
contain a small pocket watch and so
convert it to be worn on the wrist.
Presented by R.T. Oliver, 1966

685 Wristwatch guard England c1914
Metal grill to protect the fragile glass of the
period which was very vulnerable in the
trenches during the First World War.
The wristwatch strap was threaded
through the lugs on the metal
protective grill.
Presented by R.T. Oliver, 1966

686 Silver bowl England 1947
Inscribed on the edge 'Time with his
scythe may sever links mature but
Wisdom, Honour, Friendship – these
endure. 1697. 1947.' Presented by the
Governor and Company of the Bank of
England in recognition of the fact that the
Clockmakers' Company was the first City
Company to acquire, in 1697, stock in the
Bank of England, which they held until the
nationalisation of the Bank in 1947.
Made by Reginald H. Hill.
See *Horological Journal*, July 1947, p 344

681a

681b

681d

Clocks and watches and other items on loan

Our Museum forms a wonderful heritage which inspires a feeling of pride in every Freeman and Liveryman. It is stressed, however, that there are many gaps in our Collection that require filling, but to do this the Company has to rely on the interest and generosity of its members and also of the public to make gifts of horological items and even deposits on extended loan. Such items include not only clocks and watches but books, MSS, pictures, watch-keys etc and also the tools used by fine craftsmen in the past.

In this connection the Company is most fortunate in being able to exhibit several items of very exceptional interest which have been loaned by Liverymen and other supporters of the Company.

687

687 Skull watch
Moysant France c1600
The large silver case is shaped like a human skull and is pierced and also engraved all over with religious and mythological scenes as well as quotations in Latin from Horace.
The mechanism, which includes a striking train, is hidden inside the skull. It has had considerable alteration and is now a conversion to lever escapement.
The silver dial, which has two hands, is engraved with a scene of Saturn swallowing his children. Signed 'Moysant Blois'.
The watch retains its original protective leather case, 76 × 82mm.
It is said to have belonged to Mary Queen of Scots, but its present mechanism is of later date than the Queen's execution in 1587.
See *Britten's Old Clocks and Watches and their Makers* (6th edition), pp 139–41; J.C. Smith, *Historical and Literary Curiosities* (1852).
On loan from G.S. Saunders

688 Table clock
R.S. Germany c1600
Drum-shaped engraved gilt-metal case. The dial has an hour ring engraved I–XII and inside this another ring engraved 13–24. Although the clock now has only one hand, there is also a minute circle 0–60 and inside it are four quarter markings I. II. III. IIII, with touch-pins. The centre of the dial is a movable alarm-setting ring. The hour-striking movement is nearly all iron with twisted pillars. The plates have many unused holes and it has evidently been much altered. There is now a verge and foliot escapement with a stackfreed to control the power of mainspring. Engraved R.S. and two signs which are not letters.
Diameter 135mm Height 65mm
On loan from Miss Hurle Bradley

689 Rolling ball clock
E. Dent & Co England c1920
The clock is of the type designed and patented by William Congreve in 1808.

The escapement is operated by a ball
rolling down a zig-zag path cut in a plate
pivoted at its centre and which tilts as the
ball reaches the end of its travel. The
movement is housed in a brass cover
designed as a Greek temple with four
Corinthian columns. There are three dials
in the pediment for hours, minutes, and
quarter minutes. Seconds are also
indicated. In one year the rolling ball
travels 2,522 miles.
On loan from Gilbert Edgar
(Past Master)

690 Watch
S. Smith & Son England HM 1899
Gold hunter case. Enamel dial with
subsidiary dials for seconds, perpetual
calendar and phases of the moon. The
watch is also a minute repeater and a
split-seconds chronograph.
Lever escapement. Free sprung.
Diam 58mm
See catalogue of S. Smith & Son,
printed c1928, p 29

691 Watch
Smiths Industries Ltd England 1959
Self-winding wristwatch in gold-plated
case with silvered dial.
Lever escapement. This is one of a few
prototypes but the model was never put
into production or sold to the public.
Signed on dial 'Smiths Imperial
Automatic. 25 jewels. Shockproof'.
Diam 35mm

The above two related items are on
loan from Colonel H. Quill, RM (Past
Master).

692 Long-case clock movement
Robert Sutton   England   1801
Painted oak dial of the Franklin-type
design. Weight-driven 8-day timepiece
with three-wheel movement contained in
brass plates 16 × 13cm. Grasshopper
escapement with steel pallet arms
actuated by a large escape-wheel of 180
teeth. Maintaining power.
Signed on dial: 'Rob.ᵗ Sutton Barton 1801'.
Robert Sutton (1774–1865) was a watch-
and clockmaker at Barton which is only
three miles from Barrow-on-Humber. In
1796 Sutton made a near copy of a
Harrison wooden regulator clock.
See also 555
Presented by Mrs K. Orr, 1974.

Index

Numbers in Roman type refer to the catalogue number of an item while numbers in italic type refer to the page numbers of introductory sections. Makers' names are included. Where doubt exists the name or number is in square brackets.

Watch,
    Chinese 495
    electronic 539
    hands 683
    hooks 677
    keys 681
    protective cover 685
    Russian [277], 377
    tuning fork 539
    wooden 277
Waterbury Co. 503, *51*, *65*
Water clock 646
Watkins, A. 449, *56*
Watson, S. 564, *77*
Watts, B. 72
Webb, B. 250
Webster, R. 62, 404

Webster, W. 74
West 480
White, J. 174
Whittaker, R. W. 501
Wightman, T. 88
Wightwick & Moss 287
Wilders, J. 220
Willeumier Frères 283
Williams, J. 280
Wilter, J. 223, 224
Winden, D. van 162
Windham & Massey 416
Windmills, T. 85, 118, 133, 135, *6*
Wolverstone, B. 43
Wood, J. 188
Wooden watch 277
Worke, J. 225

Wright, J. 37
Wright, R. 407
Wright, T. 260, 393
Wristwatch:
    early strap 684
    guard 685
    self-winding 69
    tuning-fork 539
Writs, W. 204

'Yankee' 503
Yeriaf 266
Yonge, G. 370
Young, J. 344

[Zoller, M.] 11